All-Color

The
Human Body

by Paul Lewis and David Rubenstein
Illustrated by John Bavosi

Bantam Books
Toronto · New York · London

FOREWORD

The workings of the human body are something of a mystery to many people. Yet this is the most fascinating living entity of all.

This introduction to the body, its structure and functions, is for those who wish to understand how the basic systems of the human organism work and interrelate. Explanations are detailed, without employing unnecessary medical terminology. The principles of anatomy and movement, eating and digestion, breathing and blood circulation, nervous relay and behavior, reproduction and genetics are clearly described.

This book will serve as a concise account both for those who are reading for general information and those who will go on to study the subject in greater detail.

THE HUMAN BODY

*A Bantam Book/ published by arrangement with
Grosset & Dunlap, Inc.*

PRINTING HISTORY

*Grosset & Dunlap All-Color Guide hardcover edition
published July 1971*

Bantam edition / August 1972

2nd printing .... *April 1973*   4th printing ....*July 1975*
3rd printing .... *August 1974*   5th printing ... *November 1976*
6th printing ....*August 1977*

ISBN 0-553-11296-1

Published simultaneously in the United States and Canada

Bantam Books are published by Bantam Books, Inc. Its trademark, consisting of the words "Bantam Books" and the portrayal of a bantam, is registered in the United States Patent Office and in other countries. Marca Registrada. Bantam Books, Inc., 666 Fifth Avenue, New York, New York 10019.

PRINTED IN THE UNITED STATES OF AMERICA

0 9 8 7

CONTENTS

4 **Introduction**

5 **Cells**

8 **Tissues**

14 **Circulation**

32 **Respiration**

48 **Digestion and metabolism**

76 **The urinary system**

82 **Hormones and reproduction**

106 **Blood**

120 **The nervous system**

150 **The senses**

156 **Books to read**

157 **Index**

INTRODUCTION

Imagine a machine consisting of a system of levers and cables with the capacity to lift hundreds of pounds, but able also to construct minute and intricate instruments such as the jeweled movements of watches. Suppose that this machine had both central heating and air conditioning, allowing it to range from the tropics to the poles. Imagine that it could propel itself across the land at speeds of 30 feet per second and higher, and, moreover, could function 600 feet under the sea if given helium and oxygen fuel mixtures at high pressures. Let us say that our machine could draw up plans for skyscrapers and then build them; write its own symphonies and then play them. Suppose, too, that this machine could build other machines—some capable of travels to the moon and beyond and back. Surely a machine with so many diversified properties would prove enormously helpful to mankind. The fact is that each of us possesses this miraculous machine: our own flesh and blood body. Starting with the living cell, the basic unit of the human body, the ensuing chapters create a fascinating picture of the body and its marvelous workings as understood by contemporary scientists.

Internal structure of a cell   (*Opposite*) Different types of cells

Mitochondrion

Nucleus

Nucleolu[s]

Centriole

Endoplasmic reticulum

Golgi body

CELLS

All organisms, save the simplest, the viruses, are constructed of one or more tiny units known as cells. An average adult has more than 500 trillion cells. The biggest human cell is the fly-speck-size ovum, the egg made in a woman's ovaries. At about 1/100 inch it is a giant next to certain brain cells, only 1/50 that size. Cells grow in shapes governed by the tissues where they reside. For instance, nerve- and muscle-fiber cells may exceed 3 feet in length. The cell membrane, a two-ply layer of fatty molecules called *lipids,* is porous, allowing for transfer between the cell's *cytoplasm* and the bloodstream of oxygen, nutrients and wastes. The jellylike cytoplasm contains the *nucleus* and minute structures, the *organelles.* The *mitochondrial* organelles make enzymes that prompt the respiratory process within the cell—the oxidation of carbohydrates, releasing energy. The cell's protein-manufacturing assembly line is the *endoplasmic reticulum,* a network of ribonucleic acid (RNA) molecules that weave as patterns for linking together protein chains from amino-acid units.

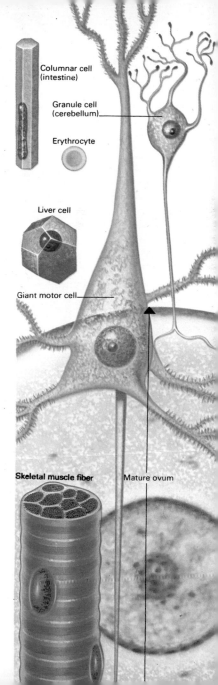

Columnar cell (intestine)

Granule cell (cerebellum)

Erythrocyte

Liver cell

Giant motor cell

Skeletal muscle fiber

Mature ovum

Human chromosomes

How cells divide

Beginning from a single fertilized ovum, the body eventually numbers hundreds of trillions of cells. The reproduction of new cells from old is necessary for such growth. Moreover, the body also replaces cells that wear out. New cell formation occurs through cell division, and the key to cell division is the nucleus (see illustration, bottom page 4).

The nucleus is a 'command center' that uses stored information in regulating various cellular activities. This information is 'coded' and stored in the *genes*—molecules of deoxyribonucleic acid (DNA) linked in chromosomal chains, or *chromatids*. When a cell splits, identical DNA, carrying the so-called 'genetic code', is given to the new cell. Here at work is the familiar process of heredity, in which the genes assure that like produces like. Most cells divide by *mitosis,* as illustrated on page 7. First, the parent nucleus makes (synthesizes) new DNA, forming identical new chromosomal chains for the new nucleus. DNA-synthesis requires about eight hours, and cell division follows afterward in about two hours. Rapid reproducers, like intestinal cells, split about once a day, while other body cells may not fission for months. In mitosis, all 46 human chromosomes (in 23 pairs) are inherited by the new cell. In human reproductory glands, however, a special type of division called ˙*meiosis* occurs: only half the number of chromosomes, 23, are made. Thus when sperm and ovum unite, the fertile cell will contain the full 46 paired chromosomes, getting half from each parent.

1 Early interphase. Chromatids are single. 2 Late interphase. Chromatids double to form identical chains attached to the parent chromatids only at their central points.

3 Prophase. Chains coil up. Centrosome splits into two parts which go to opposite ends of nucleus, remaining linked by spindle of rays of cytoplasm. Nucleus boundary disappears. 4 Early metaphase. Chromosomes are lined up and attached to spindle at central points.

5 Late metaphase. Double chains begin to split. 6 Early anaphase. The daughter chromosomes part, as if drawn by the spindle.

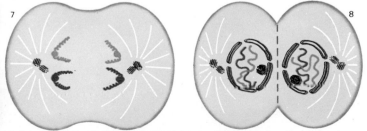

7 Late anaphase. 8 Telophase. Chromosomes elongate. Nucleus boundaries appear. There are now two cells, each with 46 chains of genes like its parent.

Simple epithelium lining arteries

Columnar epithelium as found in alimentary tract

Ciliated columnar epithelium as found in nostrils

Transitional epithelium as found in bladder

TISSUES

Epithelial tissues

Epithelia are the sheets of tissue which cover and protect all external and internal surfaces of the body. They consist essentially of layers of cells packed together and lying on top of connective tissue. There are many different varieties of epithelium, from thick tough skin to the delicate lining of the lung alveoli, and with this diversity of structure goes a wide range of functions.

The simplest epithelia are formed of a single layer of flattened cells resembling a tiled pavement. Such cells are found in many places, including the tubules of the kidney, the inside of the eardrum, and the lungs, while similar cells line blood vessels and the pleural and peritoneal cavities. They are thin enough to allow the transfer of materials through them,

Stratified squamous epithelium as found in skin

while in the pleura and peritoneum they provide frictionless surfaces. The lining of the alimentary tract—from lower esophagus to rectum—is much thicker, being composed of a layer of taller cells which under the microscope look like a row of books from the side and a honeycomb from the top. These cells secrete enzymes and mucus. A similar layer is found in the breathing passages, covered with fine hairs, or *cilia.* Glands from which secretions drain through a duct are formed from ingrowths of epithelium. Such ingrowths vary from the simple coiled tubes of sweat glands to the many-branched structures found in salivary glands and breasts. A special type of epithelium covers the internal surfaces of the bladder. Several cell layers thick, it can be stretched without the appearance of gaps; hence, it is waterproof.

Blood as a tissue

The liquid part of the blood is known as *plasma.* The plasma is a weak solution of salts, dissolved oxygen molecules, and other substances. Chief among the solid matter or tissue of the blood is the *red cell,* which lacks a nucleus. The red cells are manufactured in the bone marrow. They contain an iron compound, *hemoglobin,* which serves to transport oxygen and carbon dioxide between the lungs and the body cells. Oxygenated heme is red in color. Heme carrying carbon dioxide is bluish. The white cells, or *leucocytes,* also carried by the blood, possess nuclei; their function is to fight harmful bacteria. Small particles called *platelets* are responsible for clotting. In later sections the circulation of the blood and the function of its various components are discussed in considerable detail.

Blood cells

Platelet

Red corpuscle

White corpuscle

Hair

Epidermis

Dermis

Subcutaneous
fat

Sweat gland   Hair follicle

Section of skin

Skin

The skin is the largest, thickest and most complex epithelial tissue in the body and is an organ of heat regulation as well as one of protection. It has two parts—the horny outer *epidermis* and the soft inner *dermis,* in which are embedded hair follicles and sebaceous and sweat glands.

In all people except albinos, brown granules of *melanin* are contained in the deepest cells of the epidermis. This pigment is made in special cells (*melanoblasts*) lying just below the epidermis; melanoblasts are activated by ultraviolet light, producing freckles and tanning in light skins.

Hairs grow upward from the dermis and are continually shed and replaced, new hairs forming in old follicles. Attached to the follicles are strands of smooth muscle. When they contract, they pull the hairs upright (trapping air and creating a heat-insulating layer), causing gooseflesh.

Sebaceous glands open into hair follicles and lubricate the skin with their oily secretion, which is produced by the disintegration of the glandular cells. They are distinct from sweat glands, the watery secretion of which evaporates on the surface, helping to cool the body. The dermis has many blood vessels, and the sweat glands are especially well supplied.

Loose connective tissue 1 Macrophage. 2 Mast cells. 3 Reticular cell.
4 Fat cells. 5 Fibroblast. 6 Plasma cell. 7 Monocyte. 8 Lymphocyte.
9 Collagen fibers. 10 Elastic fibers. 11 Blood vessel

Connective tissue

Connective tissue has relatively few cells surrounded by a
mass of intercellular material and fibers. It provides a mobile supporting framework for more specialized tissues.

In the loose tissue beneath the dermis there is a viscous
ground substance criss-crossed by branching elastic fibers
and bundles of tough collagen fibers. Between these are a
variety of cells, including spindle-shaped *fibroblasts* (which
make collagen); *macrophages* (amoeba-like defensive
cells, capable of *phagocytosis*—engulfing foreign or dead
material); *plasma cells* and *lymphocytes* (involved in immunity); and *mast cells* (which manufacture the *ground
substance*). Capillary blood vessels and nerves pass
through connective tissue, and fat cells are also found.

Tendons are formed of strong white fibrous tissue composed of parallel bundles of collagen fibers. Yellowish
elastic tissue is found in the trachea, large arteries and
spinal ligaments, and is tough but springy.

Most of the fat in the body is stored in connective tissue
inside special cells, the cytoplasm of which is stretched into
a thin bubble. In fatty areas all other elements are dis-
placed, resulting in a uniform appearance and a soft
texture.

Capillary   Osteocyte (bone cell)

The tissues of the skeleton

Two types of firm material, bone and cartilage, form the inner skeleton of the human body. In early fetal life, all 'bones' are made of cartilage; this is more flexible than bony tissue and is later replaced in all weight-bearing parts.

Most bones have a compact outer layer and a porous inner part. Some long bones are hollow with a central marrow cavity. All have a fibrous covering, the *periosteum*, containing cells which can form new bone to mend fractures. Compact bone consists of cylindrical layers surrounding intercommunicating canals, through which pass nerves and blood vessels. The bone cells are harbored in small cavities between the layers; these cavities are connected with each other by fine channels filled with cell branches. The substance between the cells is the important part of bone, for it is hard because of impregnation with crystals of minerals.

Cartilage (gristle) is semi-transparent and elastic. It is found in adults in the nose, external ear, larynx and air passages, the front part of ribs and covering the moving surfaces of some joints. It consists of a dense feltwork of fine

Structure of cartilage

collagen fibers encased in a mucoid substance and containing small isolated groups of cells. In certain parts of the body, such as intervertebral discs, it is strengthened by the incorporation of thick bundles of collagen, while in other places, like the external ear, it contains elastic fibers.

The transformation of cartilage into bone begins in the fetus with the appearance of centers of bone production in each piece of cartilage. Bone-forming cells make a fibrous matrix on which calcium is deposited, and which extends outward until virtually complete replacement has occurred. A plate of proliferating cartilage cells, however, remains near the ends of bones until adolescence; the newly made cartilage calcifies, enabling the bones to lengthen.

The joints between bones are of several different types. Some allow no movement, like the fibrous junctions between skull bones. Others, like the vertebral joints with their intervening discs, permit limited bending and rotation. In ball-and-socket (hip) and hinge (knee) joints, a lubricated membrane and cartilaginous discs give free movement.

Fibrous skull joint

Vertebral joint

Ball-and-socket joint

Hinge joint

CIRCULATION

The anatomy of the thorax

The chest, or thorax, is enclosed below by the diaphragm and above by the clavicles, upper ribs and lower neck vertebrae. It contains and protects the heart and lungs, which are surrounded by a flexible wall composed of ribs connected by intercostal muscles and covered with soft tissues and skin.

The 12 thoracic vertebrae, behind, and the curved ribs and sternum, at the sides and in front, form a protective bony framework for the vital organs of the chest. Greater protec-

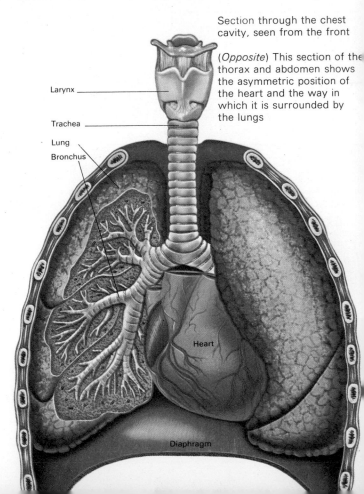

Section through the chest cavity, seen from the front

(*Opposite*) This section of the thorax and abdomen shows the asymmetric position of the heart and the way in which it is surrounded by the lungs

Larynx

Trachea

Lung

Bronchus

Heart

Diaphragm

tion would come from a solid chest cage, as is found in some invertebrates, but a rib-cage has the advantages of greater mobility and less weight.

The diaphragm is a muscular and fibrous sheet which divides the thoracic from the abdominal cavity. Its margins are attached to the inner surfaces of the lower ribs, and the contractile muscle fibers run horizontally and radially toward the center of the chest where they become tough, inelastic and fibrous. Several important structures pass through the diaphragm. These include the esophagus, leading to the stomach; the descending aorta, which carries arterial blood to the abdomen and the legs; and the inferior vena cava, through which blood returns from these parts to the heart. Each has its own opening in the diaphragm, and vagus nerves travel down with the esophagus, and sympathetic nerves and lymph channels with the aorta, while the nerves of the diaphragm are close to the upper part of the inferior vena cava.

The heart sits on the front and center of the diaphragm,

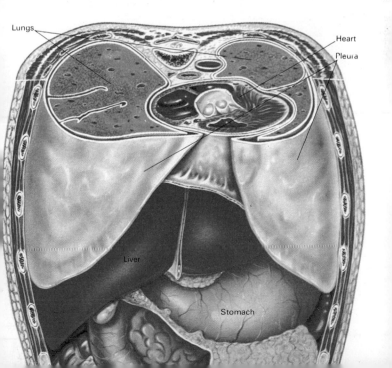

Lungs

Heart

Pleura

Liver

Stomach

enclosed in a protective membranous bag, the *pericardium*. The lungs fill the rest of the thoracic cavity. The tip of the heart's left ventricle is in contact with the inside of the chest wall between the fourth and fifth ribs, a few inches to the left of the sternum; when the left ventricle contracts, a localized pulsation can be felt at the apex point — the *apex beat*. When the heart is enlarged, the apex beat is enlarged outward beyond its normal limit, so as to be felt below the fifth rib.

The aorta emerges from the left ventricle and rises for two to three inches before arching backward toward the spine and descending. The arch of the aorta passes to the left of the trachea and above the left pulmonary artery.

The functions of the circulation

The heart and blood vessels form a completely closed system. Blood leaves the heart and travels via the aorta to strong, muscular, arterial vessels, which divide into smaller muscular vessels called the arterioles. These progress into tiny, thin-walled capillaries, which ramify between the cells and supply them

This cross-section shows the relative thickness of the walls of a vein and an artery

The arterio-venous bridge

The circulatory system

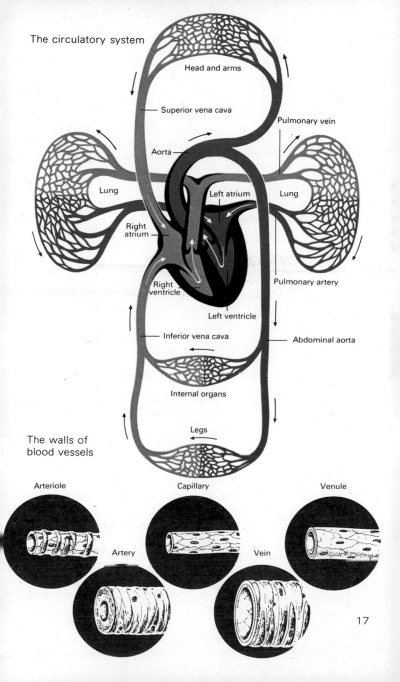

Head and arms

Superior vena cava

Pulmonary vein

Aorta

Lung

Left atrium

Right atrium

Lung

Right ventricle

Left ventricle

Inferior vena cava

Abdominal aorta

Internal organs

Legs

The walls of
blood vessels

Arteriole

Capillary

Venule

Artery

Vein

with oxygen, glucose, hormones and other essential substances.

The function of the circulation is to deliver energy and food supplies to each cell and to remove waste products of cell metabolism like carbon dioxide. If such products were not removed, they would interfere with the normal workings of the cells and ultimately cause their death; but the circulation removes wastes from where they are produced and carries them to the lungs, kidneys and liver, where they are excreted or changed into less toxic substances.

The capillaries coalesce into venules, leading into larger veins which eventually drain into the right atrium of the heart by way of the two venae cavae.

The chambers and valves of the heart

The heart has four chambers, the right and left atria and the right and left ventricles. The ventricles empty blood into the pulmonary arteries and aorta, while the atria collect blood from veins. Arterial blood pressure is much higher than venous and the walls of the ventricles are correspondingly thicker than those of the atria.

The aortic and pulmonary valves are placed at the outflow of the left and right ventricles, respectively; mitral and tricuspid valves serve to seal off the adjacent atria. The cusps of the valves float freely in the blood passing through them, their position depending on the pressure difference on their two sides. When the valves close, the cusps come together to form a blood-tight membrane.

Blood from the tissues enters the right atrium via the venae cavae. This blood has relatively little oxygen and a relatively high carbon dioxide content (partial pressures 40 mm and 46 mm of mercury, respectively), and it passes through the tricuspid valve into the right ventricle, from where it goes into the pulmonary artery and to the lungs. The blood pressure on the right side of the heart is low (25 mm of mercury in the ventricle) and so the chambers are relatively thin-walled. In the lungs carbon dioxide is removed and the blood oxygenated. Blood returns to the left atrium via the pulmonary veins, and now has relatively more oxygen and less carbon dioxide (100 mm and 40 mm, respectively). It then flows through the mitral valve into the thick left ventricle and is pumped through the aortic valve into the aorta for bodily distribution. Pressure in the aorta is about 120 mm of mercury. Heart muscle is known as *myocardium;* the linings of the valves as *endocardium.*

(*Opposite*) Section of the heart showing chambers, major vessels and valves

The left ventricle operates at higher blood pressures than the right. This section through the ventricle at dotted line on opposite page shows clearly the thicker muscle wall of the left ventricle.

The blood supply of the heart

The right and left coronary arteries supply blood to the heart muscle. They arise from the aorta just after its origin from the left ventricle. The right coronary artery curves around the right border of the heart, passing between atrium and ventricle, and supplies most of the back and the under-surface of the heart with blood. The left coronary artery runs in the opposite direction to supply the left side of the heart, and it gives off a large branch which descends in front between the ventricles and provides blood for this region. Disease which causes narrowing or partial blockage of these arteries is responsible for heart attacks ('coronaries').

The cardiac cycle

The cardiac cycle is the name given to the series of events which occurs in a single heart beat. During each cycle the two atria contract together and then the ventricles contract, and blood is forced from the atria into the ventricles and from these into the aorta and the pulmonary artery. This takes place 50 to 80 times a minute in normal adults.

The period in which the ventricles are contracting is called *systole* and that in which they relax *diastole*. Immediately after systole the atria begin to fill with blood (see *a* below). Tricuspid and mitral valves are closed at this time. The pressures in the ventricles fall and the pressures in the atria rise. As soon as the pressures in the atria exceed those in the ventricles, the tricuspid and mitral valves float open. The

a. Atria fill with blood.

b. Contraction of atria forces more blood into ventricles.

The blood supply of the heart

ventricles, now relaxed and dilated, fill with blood and the cardiac cycle begins with contraction of the atria (*b*), which forces more blood into the ventricles. Almost immediately the ventricular muscle contracts. The pressures in the ventricles rise very rapidly and soon exceed those in the atria, so that the mitral and tricuspid valves are forcibly closed. Because ventricular pressures exceed those in the aorta and pulmonary artery, the aortic and pulmonary valves are thrown open and blood is forced smoothly through them into the arteries (*c*). Then the ventricles relax, pressure falls, the aortic and pulmonary valves close (*d*) and the cycle begins anew. In a single day, the heart pumps the adult's average 10 pints of blood through 1,000 complete circuits— pumping a total of 5,000 to 6,000 quarts of blood.

c. Ventricles force blood into aorta and pulmonary artery.

d. Valves close

Excitation of the heart

The muscular contractions of the heart are produced by regular electrical impulses originating in a tiny area of muscle, the sino-atrial node or 'pacemaker', at the junction of the right atrium and superior vena cava. This node contracts spontaneously, and this stimulates the walls of the atria, from which the contractile impulse reaches another special area, the atrio-ventricular node. From here the impulse travels at about four yards per second in the fibers of the 'bundle of His'—muscle fibers adapted for fast conduction—and spreads throughout the ventricles, stimulating them to contract.

The heart rate depends on the activity of the sino-atrial node, but if this is damaged the atrio-ventricular node takes over its function. This node has its own contraction rate of 35 to 45 per minute, which is unaffected by any external influences. In contrast, the sino-atrial node is controlled by the vagus nerve (which slows its rate) and the sympathetic nerves (which increase it).

The cardiac action initiated by the sino-atrial node can be recorded in the form of an *electrocardiogram* (EKG). Electrical activity of each part of the heart has its own waveform. The P-wave and the QRS-waves come, respectively, from the contracting atria and ventricles, while the T-wave coincides with relaxation of the ventricles. Disease of the heart usually produces changes in the wave pattern.

The impulse spreads out from the sino-atrial node. The electrocardiogram trace (*below*) shows the change in electrical potential across the heart during one cardiac cycle.

Sino-atrial node

Atrio-ventricular node

R

P

Q S

T

0   0·2   0·4   0·6   0·8

Time (seconds)

Heart sounds and murmurs

Passage of blood through the irregularly shaped heart cavities is turbulent, with fluid eddies which cause vibrations. These can be heard with a stethoscope as heart sounds and murmurs. In the normal heart, two sounds are produced, the second being shorter and sharper than the first. The first sound is due to closure of the mitral and tricuspid valves at ventricular systole, while the second results from closing of the aortic and pulmonary valves as the ventricles relax.

Disease of the valves roughens their surface and increases turbulence, so that vibrations may be produced while the valves are open, that is, between the heart sounds. Such vibrations constitute heart murmurs, and doctors can often pinpoint the damaged valve by careful study of the murmur. Sometimes babies are born with an incomplete partition between atria and ventricles, and passage of blood through this 'hole in the heart' is another cause of murmurs. Increased turbulence, with resultant murmurs, is not always due to heart disease, but may occur in health, especially in children.

Taking an electrocardiogram

The correlation between events in the cardiac cycle

Vol. = Volume of left ventricle
Jug. = Pressure in jugular vein
Atr. = Intra-atrial pressure
Vent. = Intra-ventricular pressure
Elect. = Electrocardiogram
Aorta. = Intra-aortic pressure
Car. = Pulse in carotid artery
Rad. = Pulse in radial artery
S.O. = Opening and closing of
S.C. semilunar (aortic) valves
A.V.O. = Opening of atrio-
ventricular valves

Time in 1/10 seconds

The electrical activity corresponding to atrial and ventricular excitation immediately precedes the respective atrial and ventricular systoles. Opening and closing of the semilunar valves are critical for the aortic pressure changes and changes in ventricular volume. The pressure wave is delayed and distorted along the arterial tree.

Normal blood pressure

'Blood pressure' is the pressure of blood in the arteries and is a measure of the tension in the arterial wall produced by the blood forced through from the heart. This pressure depends on two factors—the output of the heart and the resistance to flow provided by the smaller arteries and arterioles. In young adults blood pressure normally reaches 120 mm of mercury during systole and falls to 80 mm in diastole.

Cardiac output is the volume of blood pumped out per minute, and this will obviously increase if the heart rate goes up. Resistance to blood flow depends on the diameter of the smaller muscular vessels, which can be constricted by activity of the sympathetic nervous system, itself influenced by the vasomotor center. This center is in the hind-brain, and it sends out impulses which pass down to the sympathetic nerves supplying the vessels. It is regulated by nervous messages, especially those coming to the brain from sensitive pressure receptors in the wall of the aorta, and normally these receptors are sending signals to the center all the time. Blood pressure is thus constantly monitored and adjusted to a more or less steady level. Any increased pressure in the aorta, for example, from an increased cardiac output, is signaled to the vasomotor center, which suppresses sympathetic activity—causing relaxation of small vessels and a fall in resistance to flow. Conversely, a fall in aortic pressure produces increased activity in the center and stimulation of sympathetic nerves; the arterioles contract and their resistance increases, helping to maintain the blood pressure at its usual level.

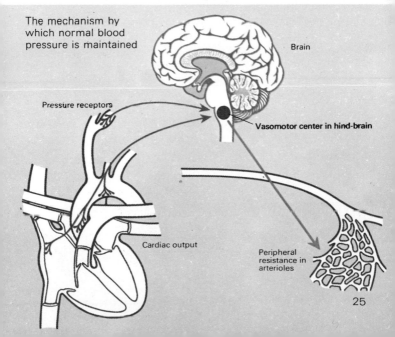

The mechanism by which normal blood pressure is maintained

Brain

Pressure receptors

Vasomotor center in hind-brain

Cardiac output

Peripheral resistance in arterioles

25

High blood pressure (hypertension)

High blood pressure (hypertension) results from increased resistance to flow. This may be because vessels are narrowed or because the blood is more viscous than normal. Increased cardiac output does not cause sustained hypertension, but can produce a transient rise.

Emotional stresses of all kinds are reflected in the blood pressure. Excitement, agitation or annoyance stimulate sympathetic nervous activity, which accelerates the heart and contracts arteriolar muscle, both of which effects cause hypertension. A heated argument can raise blood pressure to as much as 240 mm (systolic)/130 mm (diastolic)—normal values are 120/80.

Another important factor is the influence of certain hormones, especially *noradrenaline*. As described later in the book, this substance is produced by the medulla of the adrenal gland and it causes contraction of the muscular walls of blood vessels. If too much is in the circulation, this contraction results in a prolonged rise of blood pressure. This may occur with a tumor of the adrenal medulla, and if this is removed the blood pressure may return to normal.

Kidney disease plays an important part in producing high blood pressure, for the damaged kidney secretes a substance called *renin* which is converted in the blood to another substance which is very active in producing arteriolar contrac-

Factors leading to high blood pressure

Brain

Adrenal gland   Aldosterone   Emotions

Kidney   Noradrenaline

Renin   Arteriole

This transverse section of a small artery in the kidney of a case of malignant hypertension shows the thickening of the vessel walls.

(*Below*) Severe hypertension can damage the retina of the eye. (*Left*) Normal appearance and (*right*) severe hypertension, with hemorrhage of blood vessels and flecks of hard exudate.

tion. Renin is secreted in a wide variety of kidney diseases, many of which cannot be cured. One, however, which can be treated is narrowing (stenosis) of the renal artery; here large quantities of renin are produced and the hypertension may be severe, but surgical correction of the narrowing often results in a cure.

The blood becomes more viscous when the proportion of red blood cells increases. This occurs in *polycythaemia*. A

27

greater force than normal is needed to push the thick blood through the vessels, and this is shown as an increased arterial pressure.

Finally, overloading of the circulatory system with blood may cause hypertension, for the vessels become filled beyond their normal capacity. The volume of blood may increase as a result of salt and water retention by the kidneys, as occurs when tumors of the adrenal cortex secrete aldosterone.

Progressive changes in the circulatory system occur with age. The gradual silting up and hardening of arterial and arteriolar vessels lays increasing strain on the aging heart.

Shock

Shock, in the medical sense, is a condition characterized by prolonged low blood pressure, rapid pulse, sweating, cold hands and feet and eventually loss of consciousness. These features are a result of the body's tendency, when the total volume of blood is too small, to divert blood to the organs which above all others need oxygen and glucose—the brain and kidneys. Under normal conditions about 15 percent of the output of the heart goes directly to the brain and 25 percent to the kidneys. The supply to muscles accounts for about 20 percent of the cardiac output; yet muscles make up two-fifths of the total body weight, so on a simple weight-for-weight basis, brain and kidney blood flow is much the greater.

When the volume of circulating blood is low, as occurs after severe rapid bleeding from gross injuries, or after severe

The reaction of the body to rapid bleeding

Rapid bleeding

water loss (as in acute diarrhea), the circulation reacts by selectively shunting blood to the brain and kidneys. In order to maintain blood pressure the small vessels in muscle and skin contract—in response to stimuli from the vasomotor center—and thus a shocked patient appears cold and white. The adrenal glands are stimulated and pour out adrenaline and noradrenaline, while sympathetic nerves are overactive. An increased heart rate and sweating are two of the results. If bleeding or fluid loss continues, despite the increased heart rate and severe arteriolar constriction, blood pressure cannot be maintained. The blood supply to the brain drops and consciousness is lost. Unless blood volume is rapidly returned to normal, permanent brain damage and death will ensue.

The lymphatic system

Much of the blood's water is squeezed out through capillary walls by arterial pressure, forming a clear fluid called *lymph*. Seeping through tissues, lymph bathes cells with dissolved foods and oxygen molecules and eventually rejoins the blood-stream through a network of *lymphatic channels*. In the lymphatic network are located glands, or *nodes*, where disease-fighting white cells and antibodies are manufactured. Passing through infected tissue, the lymph picks up viruses and bacteria, transporting them to the nodes through which it passes on its return journey to the circulatory system. At the nodes, swelling may occur, reflecting a local fight against infection.

The adrenals are stimulated to produce adrenaline and noradrenaline.

Adrenal gland

Kidney

Heart rate increases.

Arterioles in skin and muscles contract.

Fainting

Fainting is loss of consciousness in the presence of an adequate circulating blood volume, and is due to a short-lived decrease in blood flow to the brain.

The blood in the veins is helped on its way back to the heart by the contractions of the limb muscles, especially those in the legs, which squeeze the veins and act as a pump. Venous pressure depends on gravity, and this muscle pump prevents blood accumulating in the legs in the upright position. If someone stands still for a long time, the leg muscles are not very active and so blood tends to pool there. The heart can only circulate the blood it receives, and the fall in the volume of blood returning to the heart may be great enough to decrease the cardiac output to the point where the blood flow to the brain suffers and unconsciousness follows. This is why soldiers often faint on the parade field.

Fainting may also occur when the heart rhythm is abnormal, for such abnormality may also lower the cardiac output. 'Vaso-vagal attacks' are faints especially common in young girls: here

(*Above*) The muscle pump. Contraction of the muscles compresses the vein, forcing the blood through the upper valve, while the lower valve prevents backflow.

(*Left*) When a person is in a standing position for a long time, blood pools in the legs. (*Below*) After fainting, the return of blood to the heart from the veins is no longer impeded.

it is thought that emotional upset causes increased activity of the vagus nerves, which slow the heart and reduce its output. In some heart diseases the pacemaker's conducting system is damaged and unable to function, so that the ventricles beat at their own rate of 35 to 45 per minute. The result is 'heart block', and this slow rate may be inadequate for brain blood supply, so that attacks of unconsciousness frequently occur. These can sometimes be corrected by inserting an artificial pacemaker, an electrical device which stimulates the heart to contract rhythmically at a normal rate.

If the result of unconsciousness is falling to the ground, the body becomes horizontal. In this position the effect of gravity impeding venous return and pooling blood in the legs disappears, and the flow of blood to the heart from the veins is improved. Cardiac output increases, the blood supply to the brain returns to normal and consciousness is restored.

There are a variety of types of pacemaker. Shown here is a P-wave pacemaker, which takes over when the sino-atrial node fails to evoke the natural QRS response. It amplifies the P-wave, delays it for an appropriate interval and generates a pulse which evokes the QRS-wave.

The front of the thorax. To the left the
lung is seen through the ribs, while on
the right the ribs and intercostal muscles are shown.

RESPIRATION

The events in breathing

Breathing supplies the body with oxygen and removes carbon
dioxide from it. Energy is produced in the cells through the
oxidation of carbohydrates; carbon dioxide is a by-product of
energy release, and if allowed to build up it will poison the
cells.

Ventilation of the lungs is brought about by contraction of
the diaphragm and to a lesser extent the intercostal muscles.
When its fibers contract, the diaphragm moves downward.
During quiet breathing the range of movement is one-half to
one inch. When oxygen requirements are greater, breathing

becomes deeper and faster and the movement of the diaphragm increases three- to fourfold. The intercostal muscles are attached to the upper and lower margins of the ribs. They are in two layers, with fibers running in different directions, so arranged that when they contract they pull the ribs closer together. Because of the way in which the ribs are jointed to the vertebrae this conduction rotates each rib upward and outward, like a bucket handle, and a similar movement of all the ribs produces expansion of the chest. Although most of the work of breathing is done by the diaphragm, the intercostals can take over completely if the diaphragm becomes paralyzed.

At the start of a breath, just before breathing in, the pressure inside the lungs is the same as the atmospheric pressure (760 mm of mercury). Then the intercostal muscles contract, moving the rib cage upward and outward, and at the same time the diaphragm contracts and descends. As a result the size of the chest cavity is increased and the intrathoracic pressure falls by 2 to 3 mm of mercury. At this stage the atmospheric pressure is more

Air in

Rib cage

Lung

Diaphragm

The chest and diaphragm movements in breathing

Air out

than the pressure inside the chest; since the gases in the lungs are in continuity with those outside, air rushes into the lungs to equalize the pressure difference.

At the end of each inhalation the diaphragm and intercostals relax. The diaphragm and chest wall return to their previous positions, and this fall of chest volume, together with the elasticity of the lungs, forces used air back into the atmosphere. In quiet breathing the pressure within the lungs varies from −3 mm of mercury (relative to atmospheric pressure) in inhalation to +3 mm during expiration.

Air, which contains about 20 percent oxygen and 79 percent nitrogen, is breathed in through the mouth and nose, passes into the larynx, which is guarded by the epiglottis, and enters the major airway, the *trachea*. This is a firm tube held open at all times by crescents of tough cartilage arranged one above the other. These rings do not meet at the back, and the trachea is composed behind of fibrous tissue. In section the trachea is D-shaped, the posterior part — in front of the esophagus — being flattened.

(*Left*) Section through face and neck. (*Right*) Highly magnified section of nasal lining showing ciliated cell and mucus glands. The sticky mucus catches airborn particles and the cilia move the film of mucus toward the nostrils.

Turbinates

Pharynx

Epiglottis

Esophagus

Trachea

Cilia   Mucus gland   Cells

In the chest the trachea divides into the two main *bronchi,* right and left, which are also cartilaginous. These divide further into branches supplying the lobes of the lungs. Thus on each side there are upper and lower lobe bronchi. The right lower lobe bronchus gives off a branch to the middle lobe; on the left the counterpart to this is the lingular bronchus, which comes from the upper lobe bronchus. These air channels branch again and again, and their smallest offshoots, which are only a few thousandths of a millimeter in diameter, open finally into blind-ended cavities called *alveoli.*

The lungs are encased by the *pleura,* a very thin glistening membrane which enables them to move freely and without friction inside the chest wall. The pleura has two layers: the outer lines the rib cage and intercostal muscles and the inner covers the pulmonary lobes, the two layers joining where the bronchi and blood vessels enter the lung. Normally they are closely pressed against each other, but there is always a potential space, the pressure in which is sub-atmospheric. This space can fill with air or fluid if the pleura becomes inflamed or injured, while pleurisy, accompanied by chest pain on breathing, results from an inflammatory roughening of these normally smooth surfaces.

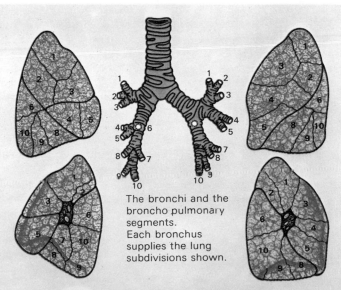

The bronchi and the broncho pulmonary segments. Each bronchus supplies the lung subdivisions shown.

Microscopic section of alveoli of lung

The movement of gases into the lungs

The alveoli, the blind openings of the terminal bronchioles, are lined by a single thin layer of cells on a fine basement membrane, attached to which are the walls of capillary blood vessels. The distance from the air in the alveoli, which communicates with the atmosphere, to the blood in these capillaries, is no more than a thousandth of a millimeter.

The air in the lungs is constantly replenished in breathing, but in fact only a fraction of the total lung volume is exchanged with each breath. The lungs of an adult man contain about six quarts of air. About half a quart is breathed in and out in quiet respiration, but up to four or five quarts can be exhaled with a great effort after as deep an inhalation as possible. This is the so-called vital capacity; it decreases with age and decrepitude and is increased in athletes. The rate at which this air can be expelled is a useful measure of the state of the lungs. Usually 80 percent of the vital capacity can be exhaled within one second, but disease of the airways (and even smoking just one cigarette) can reduce this markedly.

Movement of fresh air into the alveoli is essential for the oxygenation of venous blood arriving in the alveolar capillaries from the right side of the heart. The blood in the

Lung capacities in deep breathing and normal breathing

capillaries arrives with an oxygen tension (partial pressure) of 40 mm of mercury and an oxygen saturation of 70 percent, as well as a carbon dioxide tension of 46 mm. The fresh alveolar air has an oxygen tension of 100 mm of mercury and virtually no carbon dioxide. With these great pressure differences rapid equilibration takes place, carbon dioxide going into the alveoli and oxygen into the capillary blood. Fully oxygenated blood (tension 100 mm, saturation 100 percent) with a carbon dioxide tension of 40 mm leaves the lungs for the left side of the heart and the aorta.

(*Left*) The exchange of gases through the alveolar walls. (*Right*) A group of alveoli showing blood supply

37

The exchange of gases

Hemoglobin, which fills the red blood cells and colors the blood, is a chemical compound which readily combines with oxygen and readily releases it. The process of combination, which occurs in the lungs when blood passes through the alveolar capillaries, turns the purplish *reduced hemoglobin* into bright red *oxyhemoglobin.* The reverse process occurs in active tissues of the body and accounts for the difference in color between arterial and venous blood. Hemoglobin has an affinity for certain other substances. Of these the most important is carbon monoxide, found in coal gas and car exhaust fumes, which becomes attached very firmly, forming crimson *carboxyhemoglobin*—this prevents the carriage of oxygen by the red cells.

The degree of oxygen saturation of hemoglobin depends on the amount of the gas in the plasma surrounding the red cells. By exposing blood samples to different concentrations of oxygen and analyzing them, the way in which hemoglobin behaves can be investigated.

The oxygen dissociation curve represents the behavior of hemoglobin in the body. The S shape of the graph illustrates several important facts. In health the tension of oxygen in the alveoli is 100 mm of mercury and this produces a tension of 100 mm in the plasma in the alveolar capillaries. The hemoglobin in the red cells in these capillaries will thus be 100 percent saturated. In the fluids surrounding the cells of the body

Normal solar spectrum (1) absorption spectra of oxyhemoglobin (2) reduced hemoglobin (3) and carboxyhemoglobin (4).

the oxygen tension is the same as that inside the cells —35 to 40 mm. Fully saturated hemoglobin is unable to hold on to its oxygen, which is released and becomes freely available for use by the cells. Venous blood, coming from the capillaries surrounding the cells, is thus unsaturated (oxygen tension 40 mm, oxygen saturation 70 percent).

Cells can survive if the blood supplying them contains only 70 percent of the normal amount of oxygen. However, if for any reason the oxygen tension falls below 40 mm of mercury, the oxygen saturation of the blood falls precipitously; oxygen supply to the cells decreases to zero and they die.

The graph plots percentage of hemoglobin combined with oxygen against *dissolved* oxygen concentration in the presence of different levels of carbon dioxide. The blue curve is without carbon dioxide, the black curve corresponds to the carbon dioxide level of arterial blood and the red curve corresponds to that of venous blood. The arrows indicate shifts in *combined* oxygen content which result from changing carbon dioxide concentration *at the same dissolved oxygen concentration.* In *a* the oxygen content rises sharply as carbon dioxide is removed and in *b* the content falls as carbon dioxide is added.

Oxygen lack and excess

A fall in the body's oxygen supply can come about in two ways: the transporting system in the blood may be normal and available oxygen insufficient, or the transporting mechanism may be deficient while adequate oxygen is available. The first, which occurs more often, results from decreased oxygenation of the alveoli in the presence of normal quantities of hemoglobin. In the second, there is not enough normal hemoglobin in the blood to combine with the adequate amount of oxygen in the lungs.

Decreased alveolar ventilation often occurs in lung disease. In chronic bronchitis the walls of many of the alveoli are destroyed, resulting in an inefficient distribution of air within the lungs. In addition there are often small areas of infection, and these parts of the lung cannot be filled with air. The effect of these changes is to decrease the total surface area over which the transfer of oxygen can take place, and in consequence the blood which flows through the lungs has a smaller oxygen content than normal. Decreased oxygenation is also a feature of those lung diseases in which there is a thickening of the alveolar and capillary wall; here oxygen transfer may be markedly impaired by what is, in effect, a mechanical barrier. It is something which is found, too, in patients with a 'hole in the heart'—more accurately a hole in one of the partitions separating the chambers of the heart. If such a defect is present, deoxygenated blood may flow directly from the right atrium or ventricle to the left side of the

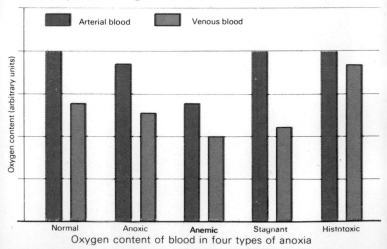

Oxygen content of blood in four types of anoxia

heart without passing through the lungs, and the arteries contain blood of low oxygen saturation. If, as a result of heart or lung disease, there is more than about 30 percent desaturation (or about 5 grams of reduced hemoglobin per 100 mls of blood), the lips and fingers appear bluish—*cyanosis*.

Another cause of poor oxygenation is decreased oxygen tension at high altitudes. Symptoms experienced by mountaineers—fatigue, lightheadedness, breathlessness—diminish after several days because the body can compensate for the low alveolar oxygen content by increasing the production of red cells and so making available more hemoglobin.

Decreased blood oxygen-carrying power occurs in anemia and when hemoglobin is unusable, as in carbon-monoxide poisoning.

Under certain conditions—especially in high concentration and with increased pressure—oxygen becomes toxic. It may inactivate some enzymes and produce cell damage, particularly in the nervous system.

Ways in which tissues may be deprived of oxygen—stagnant anoxia is essentially inadequate blood flow and in histotoxic anoxia the cells are unable to use the oxygen in the blood because certain enzymes are poisoned.

Normal

Stagnant

Anoxic

Histotoxic

Anemic

Receptors sensitive to blood pressure and to the chemical composition of the blood are situated in the large arteries. Reflex impulses from these sites affect circulation and respiration.

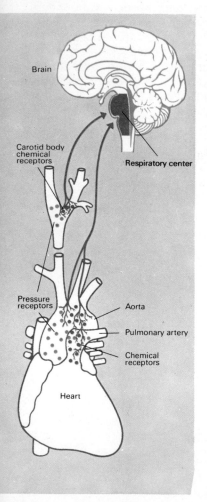

Brain

Carotid body chemical receptors

Respiratory center

Pressure receptors

Aorta

Pulmonary artery

Chemical receptors

Heart

The regulation of breathing

Breathing depends on the activity of a group of specialized nerve cells in the medulla. These cells comprise the *respiratory center*. Impulses from them pass down into the spinal cord and from there into the phrenic and intercostal nerves, causing contraction of the diaphragm and intercostal muscles and producing an inhalation. Impulses are sent off rhythmically, giving rise to the normal regular pattern of respiration. This rhythmicity is influenced by nerve information sent back to the medulla from the respiratory muscles and from the lungs, depending on whether they are contracted, relaxed or stretched, but it is partly an inherent property of the center.

The respiratory center is under many other influences. Obviously it can be affected by voluntary activity, for breath can be held until one is severely lacking in oxygen; it is, however, impossible to commit suicide by holding the breath and clearly other involuntary factors dominate respiration. The chemical state of the blood, in interaction with neural influences, ultimately determines ventilation. The center is sensitive to change in blood oxygenation, carbon dioxide content and acidity, not only in blood that passes through it but also in blood in the carotid arteries, changes here being signaled to the brain by sensitive receptor nerves. An increased level of blood carbon dioxide stimulates the activity of the respiratory center both directly and indirectly, and a rise in acidity has the same effect. The effect of anoxia is different. Lowered oxygen content in arterial blood has an intense stimulatory influence on the carotid chemoreceptors and thus causes increased respiration; if for any reason the receptors are damaged the direct action of anoxia on the brain (depression) is seen and respirations are diminished.

Respiratory center —

Impulses to:

larynx

diaphragm

intercostal
muscles

skin

Impulses from:

nose

larynx

lungs

abdomen

The respiratory center and
incoming and outgoing
pathways

The tongue of the unconscious subject (*right*) may fall back and block the airway. To clear the airway (*left*) the head should be extended and the lower jaw forced forward.

Artificial respiration

Respiratory failure occurs when the lungs are incapable of supplying adequate oxygen to the blood or removing excess carbon dioxide from it. It exists when—with a normal hemoglobin content and a normal heart—the tension of oxygen in arterial blood falls below 100 mm of mercury and the carbon dioxide tension rises above 45 mm. Artificial respiration provides a means of treating patients whose own breathing has become inadequate for their metabolic demands. It may be needed if the airways are blocked, or in cases with severe weakness of the respiratory muscles, or with depression of the brainstem respiratory center. There

(*Left*) Mouth-to-mouth resuscitation. (*Right*) External cardiac compression. Striking the heart sharply may stimulate it into beating. If there is no response, continue with mouth-to-mouth resuscitation.

are several methods, which can be used for first aid after drowning, smoke inhalation or other accidents.

Mouth-to-mouth resuscitation is simple and effective. The operator breathes in deeply, and then, while holding the patient's nose, he puts his mouth over the patient's mouth and exhales fully. He then allows the patient to exhale. This is repeated 20 times per minute.

With the *Holger-Nielsen* technique, the patient is placed flat on his front. The chest is then compressed with two hands to the count of four. This expels air—and water—from the lungs, and is followed by relaxation, while counting from five to eight, to produce an inflow of air.

The Holger-Nielsen method. After making sure the airway is free, the operator places his hands on the patient's back (*left*) just below the shoulder blades and exerts steady pressure to the count of four. The operator releases pressure (*right*) by rocking back and lifting the patient's arms while counting from five to eight.

Paralysis of the diaphragm and intercostal muscles, which may occur in severe poliomyelitis, necessitates some form of mechanical aid for breathing. In such circumstances *intermittent positive pressure respiration* is the method now generally used. It consists basically of a bellows opened and closed regularly by an electrically driven motor and pumping air into the lungs via a tube in the trachea, usually inserted through an opening or tracheostomy. With modern equipment, normal breathing can be effectively simulated.

Temperature regulation

Health depends basically on the normal functioning of the biochemical processes of the body. The rate of all chemical reactions is influenced by heat, but biochemical reactions which involve enzymes are especially sensitive. Enzymes have an optimum working temperature—in humans this is 98.6° F. A fall of even a few degrees slows them severely, while a rise of five or six degrees begins to destroy them. The body has thermostatic mechanisms which ensure a constant temperature and therefore constancy of chemical reaction rates.

Temperature control is achieved through a balance of heat gain and heat loss. Heat gain is partly from within and partly from outside. Cellular activity involves heat production of the order of 1700 calories per day in an average-sized man. Muscular work increases this basal level of heat production tenfold or more over short spells, shivering—with repeated rapid contractions of many muscle groups—being one of the most calorific activities in normal life. Heat can also be gained from the environment either from direct solar radiation or from contact with hot air.

In cold climates losing heat usually presents no difficulty, but with a high atmospheric temperature or after strenuous work, body heat must be rapidly and efficiently dissipated. This is achieved by sweating, the body's most important means of losing heat. Over three gallons of sweat can be secreted in 24 hours. In evaporating from the skin, each quart uses up 580 calories, and the quantity of heat that can be eliminated this way far exceeds what can be removed in the breath, and by radiation, convection and conduction into the surroundings. Obviously much salt and water is lost in profuse sweating, and must be replaced if heat stroke is to be avoided.

Body temperature is regulated by the hypothalamus in the brain—nerve cells sensitive to thermal changes in the blood. A fall in blood temperature puts into action involuntary nerve impulses that produce vasoconstriction (contraction of blood vessels) and shivering; a rise in temperature provokes heat loss by vasodilatation (vessel relaxation) and sweating. Injury to this part of the brain impairs the ability to keep temperature constant.

Body temperature

37°C

39°C   35°C

Heat gained

Heat regulating center

Heat lost

Blood   Skin

Basal   Shivering

Food   Disease

Exercise

Excretion   Respiration

Skin

Sweat   Vessels

Evaporation   Conduction

Convection   Radiation

The heat balance of the body

Raising and lowering of body temperature after a hot or cold bath (readings taken in mouth)

Hot bath 105°F

Cold bath 65°F

Minutes

Temperature °F

Minutes

47

The progression of a lump of food into the esophagus

DIGESTION AND METABOLISM

Chewing and swallowing—the salivary glands

The digestion of food begins in the mouth, the teeth mechanically breaking up what is eaten, the saliva providing lubrication and the tongue mixing and molding the food in preparation for swallowing.

The incisor teeth tear off small pieces, which are ground up by the premolars and molars. Saliva enters the mouth by way of ducts from three sets of glands, the parotid, sublingual and submandibular glands. In addition to *mucin* (which lubricates), saliva contains the enzyme *ptyalin,* which starts off the chemical breakdown of starchy foods.

In the mouth, the softened, moist ball of food is shaped by the tongue and is then passed backward into the throat. Swallowing now begins, the sensitive nerve endings in the back of the mouth and pharynx setting into action a chain of complicated movements. First the soft palate rises, blocking off the nose. The vocal cords close and the larynx rises. The pharynx, narrowed by this movement, then opens up; the food mass passes backward over the epiglottis, which guards the larynx, and into the esophagus, which widens to catch it.

The esophagus

The esophagus is a muscular tube, 10 inches long, leading down from the pharynx through the chest and diaphragm to the stomach. Its wall has two muscle layers, an outer one with fibers running lengthwise and an inner one with circular fibers. It is lined in its upper two-thirds with squamous epithelium, like the mouth, and in its lower one-third with glandular, mucus-forming cells.

In its resting state the esophagus is shut by the cricopharyngeus muscle above and the cardiac sphincter below. It is relaxed, often containing a little air and secretion but nothing else. When food is swallowed and enters it from above, *peristalsis* begins. This is the name given to the slow, automatic contractions that occur along the whole length of the intestines, from esophagus to rectum, propelling their contents onward. In the case of the esophagus, two to three inches of its wall contracts and the wave of contraction then passes on toward the stomach at a rate of an inch or so per second. Peristalsis is very effective — so effective, in fact, that fluids will get to the stomach even if one is upside down.

(*Above*) The tongue mixes and molds food into an easily swallowed mass.

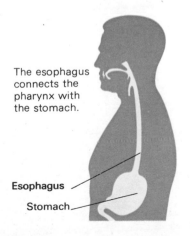

The esophagus connects the pharynx with the stomach.

Esophagus

Stomach

49

The stomach

The muscular bag of the stomach retains food for several hours, during which time digestion of protein takes place. There are three layers in the muscle coat, the middle set of fibers running obliquely, while at the exit of the stomach, the *pylorus,* the circular fibers, are thickened to form a tight ring.

The lining of the stomach contains cells which secrete the enzyme *pepsin,* hydrochloric acid and mucus. In the presence of acid, pepsin breaks down proteins to polypeptides; mucus lines the stomach and prevents it digesting itself. Acid secretion is affected by many factors, and when disturbed, peptic ulceration may result.

Smooth muscle

The muscle of the intestines (as well as certain other structures, notably blood vessels and the uterus) is called *smooth muscle* because under the microscope, unlike the skeletal muscles, it has no fine cross markings. In contrast to skeletal muscle,

Microscopic structure of stomach lining

The stomach

Esophagus

Cardiac sphincter

Muscle layers { Longitudinal / Circular / Oblique

Duodenum

Pyloric sphincter

it contracts automatically and cannot respond to an effort of will. It differs further in its relative slowness of action and in its nerve control.

Peristaltic movement is set off by distension of the hollow intestines. This affects sensory nerve cells in Meissner's plexus in the lining, and these stimulate Auerbach's plexus which lies in the muscle coats and releases *acetylcholine,* producing muscle contraction. Activity of vagus and sympathetic nerves can increase or inhibit peristalsis, but on the whole this is independent of external nervous influences.

In vomiting, the normal peristaltic motions of the esophagus and stomach are abolished. In response to gastric irritation or overfilling, or stimulation of the throat or balance organs (as in travel sickness) or any sensitive part of the body, the pylorus contracts while the stomach relaxes and all the respiratory muscles go into spasm. The increased pressure in the abdomen compresses the stomach against the diaphragm, expelling the contents. Expulsion may be helped by a reversed wave of peristalsis in the esophagus.

(*Above*) Peristalsis. (*Below*) Gastric juices, secreted in response to a signal from the brain, break down the food.

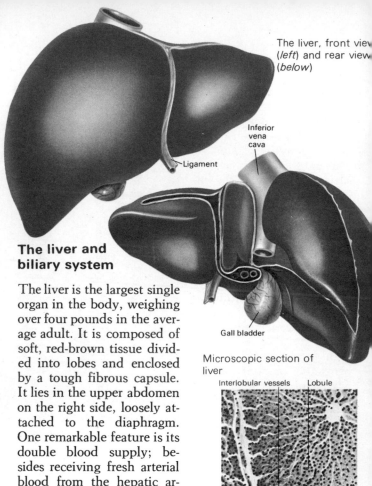

The liver, front view (*left*) and rear view (*below*)

Inferior vena cava

Ligament

Gall bladder

Microscopic section of liver

Interlobular vessels   Lobule

The liver and biliary system

The liver is the largest single organ in the body, weighing over four pounds in the average adult. It is composed of soft, red-brown tissue divided into lobes and enclosed by a tough fibrous capsule. It lies in the upper abdomen on the right side, loosely attached to the diaphragm. One remarkable feature is its double blood supply; besides receiving fresh arterial blood from the hepatic artery, which arises from the aorta, it is also fed with blood from the portal vein, carrying the products of digestion from the intestines. Its spent blood drains into the inferior vena cava via the hepatic vein.

Bile produced by the liver cells passes into the hepatic

ducts which join on the under surface of the liver into the common bile duct. This meets the duct of the pancreas in a slight expansion which opens into the duodenum (small intestine). The gall bladder is a pouch about four inches long attached to the lower surface of the liver. It is connected to the bile duct and receives, stores and concentrates bile.

Under the microscope the liver is seen to consist of millions of lobules in which uniform, many-sided cells are arranged in interconnecting sheets. Between the lobules run branches of the hepatic artery, portal vein and bile ducts, all closely bound together. Arterial and portal blood passes inward into the lobules in channels called sinusoids, which are lined by the liver cells themselves, and then drains into the central vein of the lobule, which communicates with the hepatic vein. In contrast bile passes outward in fine channels between the cells and enters the bile duct branch that is running in close proximity to arterial and portal branches. These groups of three channels, together with the adjacent parts of three lobules supplied by them, are the functional units of the liver just as the alveoli are the units of the lungs.

The gall bladder, bile duct and pancreas

patic ducts

Pancreas

Bile duct

Pancreatic duct

Duodenum

Gall bladder

Ampulla of bile duct

Lymphatic vessel, Hepatic artery, Hepatic portal vein, Hepatic bile duct, Bile canaliculi

Liver cells

(*Above*) Structure of the liver

(*Opposite left*) This shows the way in which the blood vessels branch within the liver and rejoin again. (*Right*) Fine structure of the liver

(*Below*) Shapes of separated liver cells

The functions of the liver

As well as being the largest, the liver is also the body's most versatile organ, having an extraordinarily wide range of functions. These include production, destruction and storage, and its cells contain enzymes for many chemical processes as well as vital stores of essential materials.

The substances stored by the liver include carbohydrates, fats and proteins, and the metabolism of each of these three groups of food material takes place there. *Glycogen,* which is a condensed, readily available derivative of glucose, is deposited as granules inside the liver cells and is broken down and its products released into the blood to supply energy needs. Fat is split up in the liver and also manufactured and laid down in the cells. Many nitrogenous waste products are rendered harmless in the liver by combination with other substances; *urea,* the chief nitrogen-containing product of protein metabolism, is formed there from ammonia (which is toxic to the body) and carbon dioxide. The liver cells also synthesize proteins. They make the *albumin* and part of the *globulin* in the blood plasma, and the *fibrinogen* and *prothrombin* essential for blood clotting.

Up to two pints of bile are secreted daily. It is a viscous, dark green, alkaline fluid colored by bilirubin, a breakdown product of hemoglobin, and containing quantities of cholesterol and bile salts. These salts have a detergent and emulsifying action, for their molecules have chemical groupings soluble both in watery and in fatty substances. This explains the ability of bile to enhance the absorption of fats from the intestines. When bile secretion is impaired, fat cannot be absorbed properly and is instead excreted in the feces (steatorrhea), and in addition the fat-soluble vitamins A, D and K are lost to the body.

Storage of certain vitamins is another function. Vitamin A is present in large quantities in liver fat, and vitamin D is also found (hence the value of cod-liver oil). The liver contains vitamin B_{12}, enabling the maturation of red blood cells to continue for many months after deficient diet or stomach disease deprives the body of fresh supplies.

The formation of red cells occurs in the liver in fetal life, while throughout life their destruction is partly achieved by reticulo-endothelial cells lining its sinusoids.

The pancreas and duodenum

The *peritoneum* is the shiny transparent membrane which lines the inside of the abdomen and extends over the intestines, providing lubricated surfaces which can glide against each other with next to no friction. Inflammation of the peritoneum produces the painful condition of peritonitis.

The small intestine forms a coiled, twisted mass filling the center of the abdomen. Unrolled, it is a narrow, mobile tube several feet long in life, but considerably more — 20 feet — after death, when its muscle is flaccid. It is divided into three parts, the first of which, the *duodenum,* lies at the back of the abdomen behind the peritoneum.

A C-shaped tube 10 inches long, the duodenum begins at the pylorus, passes behind the liver, in front of the right kidney and across the aorta. It encircles the head of the pancreas, secretions from which, with bile from the liver, enter it through a duct. The duodenum, like other parts of the

The anatomy of the intestines

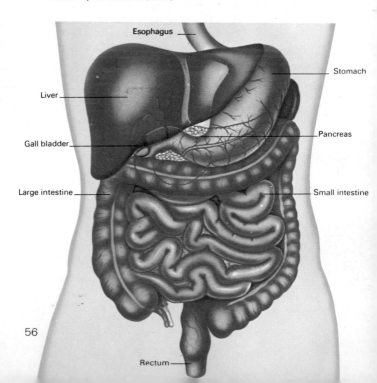

Esophagus

Stomach

Liver

Pancreas

Gall bladder

Large intestine

Small intestine

Rectum

small intestine, has an outer longitudinal and an inner circular muscle coat. Inside this is the mucous membrane, which has millions of minute finger-like projections called *villi*, the spaces between which collect the secretions from the epithelial cells. In the duodenum — but not elsewhere — are glands beneath the mucous membrane called *Brunner's glands*.

The *pancreas* is a fleshy gland 6 inches long, resembling salivary glands in structure and containing, besides the cells secreting pancreatic juice, many tiny *islets of Langerhans* (see pages 96–97). 1 to 1½ pints of its fluid are poured daily into the duodenum. It is alkaline and has enzymes which break down starch to maltose (*amylase*) and fats to glycerol and fatty acids (*lipase*). It also contains enzymes that are activated in the duodenum and split proteins into polypeptides (*trypsin* and *chymotrypsin*). Pancreatic secretion is partly under nervous control but is also stimulated by chemical substances produced in the duodenum when acid enters it from the stomach; this ensures that enough alkali is secreted to reduce gastric acidity sufficiently for duodenal digestion to continue under optimal conditions. Brunner's glands, which produce alkali and mucus, aid this neutralization and also protect the first part of the duodenum from damage by stomach acid.

(*Left*) Magnified section of the wall of the duodenum.
(*Right*) Just as the pleura envelop the lungs, so the peritoneum envelops the continually contracting intestines.

Diaphragm

Lesser peritoneal sac

Greater peritoneal sac

Brunner's glands

Circular muscle layer

Longitudinal muscle layer

Tunica serosa

The small and large intestines

From the duodenum, the second and third segments of the small intestine, the *jejunum* and *ileum,* lead into the large intestine, or *colon.* These parts of the bowels are tethered to the posterior abdominal wall by the fanshaped mesentery. The jejunum and ileum are the site of most of the process of food digestion and the absorption of nutrients into the blood. Food enters the jejunum as a slightly acid liquid and leaves as an alkaline. During this passage, which takes an average of one to two hours, virtually all nutrient material is extracted.

The secretions of the jejunum and ileum contain lipase, maltase, invertase, fructase and amylase (see pp. 60–61) and activate the pancreatic protein-splitting enzymes. Other enzymes break down polypeptides into amino acids and split nucleic acids into their components.

Absorption of digestion products begins in the duodenum and is virtually complete by the time the jejunum is reached. This removal of valuable foodstuffs results from effective enzyme action and from the efficient way with which the intestinal lining absorbs them from the cavity of the bowel. The end-products of digestion that are absorbed include glucose (from carbohydrates), amino acids (from proteins) and a milky fat emulsion.

The large intestine begins at the caecum, passes upward and across the abdomen and then down; its name changes from colon to *rectum* in its last part in the pelvis, and it ends at the *anus.* The appendix is a blind-ended, worm-like projection from the caecum. It is functionless and often fills with fecal material and becomes inflamed.

The outer longitudinal muscle of the large bowel is arranged in bands. Other obvious differences from the small intestine are a larger diameter and a puckered rather than tube-like outside. The lining secretes mucus but no digestive enzymes, for the function of the large intestine is merely the formation of feces. These are formed partly from indigestible food material like cellulose, partly from bowel secretions and partly from bacteria. While the upper reaches of the intestines are sterile, the lower parts contain many organisms which manufacture a variety of substances, including vitamin K and the compounds responsible for the odor of feces. There is little

The system of vessels which carry digestion products from the intestines. Fats are absorbed into the lymph vessels of the villi, and thence they pass by way of the lymphatic system into the blood. Other digestion products are absorbed into the blood vessels of the villi.

Heart

Lymphatic vessel

Vena cava

Liver

Stomach

Spleen

Portal vein

Large intestine

Pancreas

Small intestine

Caecum

Appendix

Rectum

Artery

Epithelium

Lymph vessel

Vein

Section of villus

Intestinal villi

FAT

Oil · Chocolate · Biscuits · Eggs · Butter · Cheese

CARBOHYDRATE

Sugar · Syrup · Bread · Apples · Potatoes · Bananas

PROTEIN

Pork · Eggs · Cheese · Beef · Mackerel

or no digestible food in the contents of the colon, which during the 12-hour journey to the rectum gradually solidifies as water is extracted and reabsorbed through the colon walls into the bloodstream. When the rectum is full, reflexive peristalsis combined with relaxation of the anal sphincter muscle permits the expulsion of solid wastes.

The sources of energy

To maintain such vital processes as breathing, blood circulation and kidney and brain function, energy is essential. This energy is derived from the three classes of foodstuffs: fat, carbohydrate and protein. *Metabolism* involves the breakdown of these foods with the release of energy and their rearrangement into the complex substances which make up the tissues of the body. Energy release and chemical rearrangement is taking place all the time, and the molecules in almost every tissue or organ are in a state of continual flux.

Carbohydrates—sugars and starch—make up the bulk of most diets; they are formed of carbon, hydrogen and oxygen with the carbon atoms joined in a ring. The simplest, such as the sugar *glucose,* have only one carbon ring; cane sugar *(sucrose)* and milk sugar *(lactose)* have two rings joined together; starch (like cellulose, which cannot be digested in the human intestine) has many ring units joined together in chains. Glucose is the carbohydrate which is metabolized to provide energy in the body. The more complex substances such as sucrose and starch must be broken down into glucose units. This is achieved by enzymes in the saliva and small intestine, as has been noted earlier. Ptyalin in saliva breaks down starch in the mouth (this is why a piece of bread chewed for a while begins to taste sweetish) while invertase, lactase and maltase in the small intestine split sucrose, milk sugar and malt sugar each into two single units.

Amino-acid molecules are made of carbon, hydrogen, oxygen and nitrogen arranged in a chain, and *proteins* are composed of many amino acids linked together chemically. Proteins occur in all tissues and are the basic, indispensible constituents of living cells, forming the bulk of the cytoplasm. The digestion of food protein begins in the stomach with pepsin and hydrochloric acid and continues in the duodenum with the action of the pancreatic enzymes. These break down the proteins into *peptide* components, which are further split into their constituent amino acids. The amino acids are absorbed into the blood.

Fats act as a shock absorber, under the skin and around vulnerable organs like the kidneys, and are also a concentrated energy store. Their molecules, containing fatty acids and glycerol, are rich in carbon and hydrogen and so produce many calories when used up in the body. In life the fat under the skin is an oily liquid, but outside the body it becomes a yellowish solid. Fats are digested in the small intestine with the aid of lipase, which disrupts their molecules, and bile salts.

Metabolism

Metabolism is the name given to the biochemical processes occurring when the body builds up living tissue from basic food materials or breaks down food to provide energy. It involves the digestion of food in the intestines, the absorbing and storage of the digested materials, their incorporation into the tissues of the body and their release and destruction to water and carbon dioxide with the liberation of energy. This destruction is demanded by the complex chemistry of the body, which requires calories to power its intricate workings. The energy produced by metabolism is not all lost as heat but is instead stored within the cells, in 'energy-rich' compounds which release their calories when needed. These compounds contain special phosphate groupings. The most important is known as ATP (*adenosine triphosphate*) and when energy is required it releases a phosphate group and a number of calories, becoming ADP (*adenosine diphosphate*). Later, when it is available, energy is used—and saved up—in converting ADP back to ATP.

Carbohydrate metabolism begins with the absorption of glucose from the hollow of the intestines through their walls and into the bloodstream. Some is carried all over the body and is metabolized by its cells, while some is stored in the liver and muscles as the complex sugar glycogen. This may later be broken down to provide glucose for the body's needs or fuel for muscular activity. When it is needed, glucose enters a 'metabolic pool' in which interplay between the products of the breakdown of carbohydrate, protein and fat takes place.

Amino acids in the blood stream may come from dietary protein digestion or tissue protein breakdown. Those that are not needed for new tissue formation are metabolized in the 'pool', with *urea*—which is excreted by the kidneys—as the nitrogenous by-product.

Nucleoproteins are compounds of protein and nucleosides, which are derived from the sugar ribose and nitrogen-containing pyrimidines or purines. The breakdown products of every component save purine enter the 'pool'.

Fat is absorbed into the blood as fine globules and is the major energy store of the body. It accounts for 10 percent of body weight, and each gram produces nearly twice as many calories as a gram of carbohydrate. Before it can enter the metabolic pool it must be split into fragments containing two carbon atoms.

Metabolic interrelations

63

Diet, energy utilization and requirements

Food must contain adequate water, calories, mineral ingredients and vitamins for health to be maintained.

Water makes up 70 percent of the body. Some is lost through the kidneys together with waste products, and further amounts are lost in breath, sweat and feces. This loss must be made good or else dehydration and death will occur.

Energy is required for all living processes. It is only at death that the cells of the body cease to need fuel. During sleep the tissues of the heart, lungs, kidneys and liver continue to work, and the muscles and brain—even though inactive—use up a quantity of energy. The fuel requirements of the body during eight hours of sleep amount to about 500 calories, the *calorie* being the unit of energy used in dietetics. (A calorie is defined as the amount of heat energy needed to raise the temperature of one gram of water by one degree centigrade.) Increasing physical activity obviously demands more energy. Thus writing at a desk uses 40 to 50 calories per hour; light housework, 100 to 150 calories; heavy work like digging, up to 300 calories; with as much as 900 calories per hour spent during a hard game of basketball.

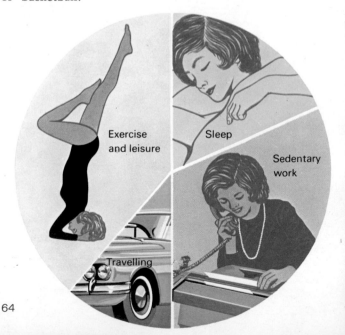

Clearly optimum calorie intake will vary markedly from person to person, depending on size (in adults the hourly resting requirement is 40 calories per square meter of body surface) and on activity. Growth is something else that uses energy; hence adolescents require at least as great a calorie intake as adults. Correct calorie intake can be worked out knowing that protein and carbohydrate each produce 4 calories and fat produces 9 calories per gram. A balanced diet should contain at least 60 grams of protein daily and enough carbohydrates and fats to provide the bulk of calorie requirements. In certain conditions it may be necessary to adjust the proportions: in diabetics carbohydrate intake must be regulated, and in kidney failure protein must be cut.

Some minerals, such as cobalt, copper and molybdenum, are needed in minute traces; others, such as sodium and potassium, are important constituents of body fluids. Calcium and phosphate are required for bone formation, iron for hemoglobin and iodine for thyroid hormones.

Calorie requirements vary greatly according to activity.

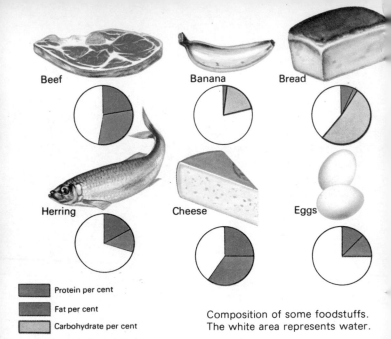

Beef   Banana   Bread

Herring   Cheese   Eggs

■ Protein per cent

■ Fat per cent

■ Carbohydrate per cent

Composition of some foodstuffs.
The white area represents water.

Normal food intake

The idea of a 'normal' diet is valuable in working out on a large scale the food requirements of a healthy adult population. In temperate climates the ideal daily food intake includes 100 grams of protein, 100 grams of fat and 400 grams of carbohydrate. Clearly carbohydrates provide most of the calories, and bread, rice and potatoes are, in this respect, important parts of the average diet. Sugar and cereals are also carbohydrate foods. Fats—including vegetable oils as well as butter, lard and drippings—provide more energy per gram and help to make the starchy foods more palatable, although they are themselves unpalatable in quantity.

Food proteins are unimportant as a source of calories but are vital because some of their component amino acids—essential for building new tissues, enzymes and hormones—cannot be manufactured in the body. Proteins are found in meat, eggs, cheese and milk as well as certain vegetable products such as beans, though plant proteins are often deficient in 'essential' amino acids. Unfortunately protein foods are expensive;

therefore poverty often unbalances the diet by restricting the protein intake. Milk is an almost perfect food; although deficient in iron, it contains protein, carbohydrate and fat and is rich in calcium, phosphate and the major vitamins.

Appetite

Exactly what regulates appetite is uncertain, but it is thought that there is a control center in the part of the brain called the hypothalamus. This center is sensitive to the amount of sugar in the blood, low sugar levels producing stimulation of appetite. Normally the blood sugar level will vary during the day, producing stimulation or suppression of appetite, but in certain abnormal states it may remain low for long periods and hunger will be experienced. Appetite is dependent on many factors, including the appearance, smell and taste of food as well as one's emotional state, illustrating that the hypothalamus is regulated by connections with the cerebral cortex as well as by blood sugar concentration.

Factors influencing appetite

Time

Hypothalamus (blood sugar)

Smell and sight

Food

Stomach contractions

Obesity and starvation

Occasionally obesity is due to adrenal overactivity, thyroid deficiency or hypothalamic tumors, but in the vast majority of cases there is no such trouble and by and large the underlying cause of obesity is unknown.

The one certain fact is that *if calorie input is greater than calorie expenditure, weight gain will occur,* but what confuses the problem are the fat people who apparently stick strictly to their diet but are never able to lose weight, and the thin ones who seem to eat excessively but remain underweight. There may be hormonal and hereditary factors in obesity, but these are uncertain. However, if calorie intake is *rigidly* controlled, as occurs in a hospital, the obese can achieve weight loss. This is highly desirable, for obesity leads to heart and kidney disease and shortening of life expectancy. Diabetes is common in the overweight, and osteoarthritis, gallstones and liver trouble are also more likely to occur. Surgical operations are more risky, and the chance of complications in the period after an operation is higher.

Perhaps half of the world is undernourished, with a diet

Comparison of diets around the world

North America

3050
63%
88

Europe an

Near East

Africa

3100
40%
93

Latin America

2500
63%
61

2350
74%
61

245
71'
76

Upper section of circle = Average daily calorie intake
Middle section of circle = Proportion of calories derived from carbohydrates
Lower section of circle = Daily intake of protein measured in grams

lacking both in total calorie content and in protein-rich foods and sometimes deficient in vitamins. The consequences of malnutrition are obvious—stunted growth, a lowered resistance to infectious diseases and a high rate of child mortality. With the population of the world ever increasing and further outstripping its food supplies, this problem is bound to get worse unless new sources of protein are found and there is unprecedented international cooperation.

Malnutrition can have other causes, however. Even with a balanced diet, it may occur if absorption of the digested food is impaired. This happens in a variety of diseases of the intestines, and here malabsorption is associated with steatorrhea. In the presence of certain chronic infections and after severe injuries or burns, the body cells may be unable to utilize dietary energy. In widespread cancer, the patient wastes away partly because the multiplying cancer cells eat up much of the available calories and protein.

In starvation—whatever the cause—stores of fat first disappear. Then body protein is used up, the muscles shrink and the patient rapidly loses weight.

(*Right*) Possible effects of obesity

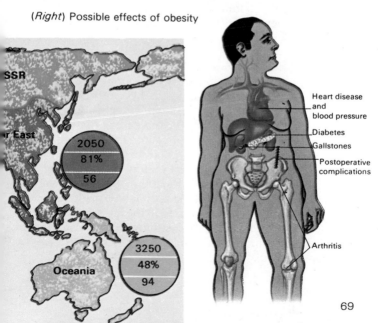

SSR

r East

2050
81%
56

Oceania

3250
48%
94

Heart disease
and
blood pressure

Diabetes

Gallstones

Postoperative
complications

Arthritis

The vitamins

Early in the twentieth century it was discovered that animals reared on artificial diets containing adequate water, protein, carbohydrate, fats and minerals, nevertheless failed to develop and grow normally. It was obvious that natural foods contained other substances that were *vital* for health; these were at first thought to be nitrogenous (that is, *amines*). We now know that few vitamins are amines, but the name has stuck.

There are at least a dozen vitamins. They can be divided into two groups, depending on whether they are soluble in fat or in water. The fat-soluble ones are vitamins A, D (anti-rickets factor), E (anti-sterility factor) and K (anti-hemorrhage factor. Vitamins of the B group and C (anti-scurvy) are water soluble.

Vitamins are essential because they are co-factors for enzyme activity; in other words they are necessary aids for the protein catalysts responsible for the processes which go on in the living body. In the absence of vitamins these catalytic systems run down and various metabolic processes may be forced to continue at greatly reduced rates or even to stop. The effects of vitamin deficiencies are thus the result of enzyme deficiencies within the tissues and cells of the body.

Vitamin A

Carotene, which is found in carrots and green vegetables, is a biological precursor of vitamin A and can be converted into vitamin A by the intestinal mucosa. The absorption of both compounds is bound up with factors influencing fat absorption from the gut, particularly the presence of bile salts in the duodenum. Vitamin A itself is present in milk, cheese, butter, eggs and liver and is stored in the body in the liver. It is needed for the regeneration of epithelial tissues, especially the skin, and it is also a precursor of rhodopsin, the light-sensitive substance of the retina. If the dietary intake is inadequate, or if the body is not able to absorb fats from the intestine, deficiency will result. This may cause thickening and dryness of the skin, partial night blindness and in severe cases opacity of the cornea.

Some sources of the principal vitamins

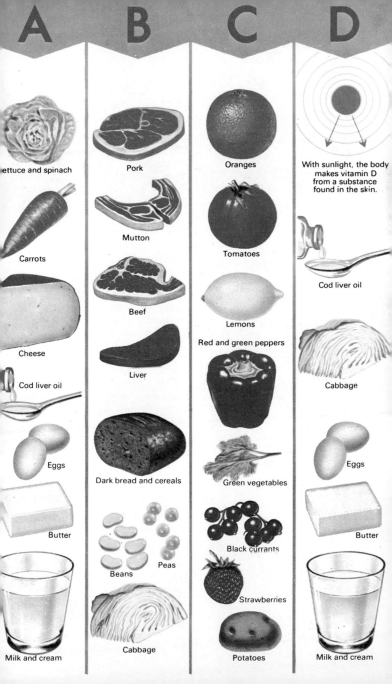

A

Lettuce and spinach

Carrots

Cheese

Cod liver oil

Eggs

Butter

Milk and cream

B

Pork

Mutton

Beef

Liver

Dark bread and cereals

Beans   Peas

Cabbage

C

Oranges

Tomatoes

Lemons

Red and green peppers

Green vegetables

Black currants

Strawberries

Potatoes

D

With sunlight, the body makes vitamin D from a substance found in the skin.

Cod liver oil

Cabbage

Eggs

Butter

Milk and cream

(*Above*) Enlargement and spread of blood vessels of the conjunctiva in riboflavin deficiency. (*Left*) 'Dry' beri-beri resulting from thiamine deficiency. Wrist drop, foot drop and wasting of lower extremities are present.

The B vitamin group includes thiamin (B_1), nicotinamid, riboflavin, pyridoxin (B_6), folic acid and cyanocobalamin (B_{12}). The first three are vital factors in carbohydrate metabolism and oxidative reactions; the fourth is involved in amino-acid metabolism, and the last two in blood formation.

Thiamin is found in beans, peas, cereals and yeast, in bran, wheat germ and rice husks and to a small extent in milk and meat. It can survive a short spell of boiling.

Thiamin deficiency causes disease of the heart, nerves and brain. The function of the heart deteriorates in its absence, and eventually heart failure occurs. One sign of this is marked ankle swelling, due to collection of fluid in the tissue under the skin (edema). This gives the condition the name 'wet' beri-beri. The heart failure clears up when thiamin is given. In 'dry' beri-beri the nerves are affected, with muscle weakness and impaired feeling in the hands and feet; recovery is slow and often incomplete after treatment, indicating that there has been permanent damage. Brain involvement from thiamin deficiency usually occurs in poorly nourished alcoholics and produces unsteadiness, loss of memory, drowsiness and coma. It may be fatal if it is not treated promptly.

Nicotinamid, which is not destroyed by cooking, is present in liver, yeast, meat and green vegetables. Deficiency causes undue sensitivity to sunlight, with severe skin damage, and also affects the cells lining the intestine and the cells of the brain, producing diarrhea and mental changes. This condition is called pellagra.

Riboflavin is obtained from meat, milk and whole-meal flour. It is relatively heat-stable but is destroyed by light. Riboflavin deficiency has no life-threatening effects. It causes changes in some epithelia, and this is most marked in the tongue, which becomes smooth, sore and purplish.

(*Left*) Pellagra dermatitis resulting from nicontinamid deficiency (*Right*) Soreness and swelling of tongue and lips in riboflavin deficiency.

A case of scurvy. The lips are held apart to show swollen bleeding gums and loosening of the teeth.

Vitamin C

For over 200 years it has been known that scurvy is due to a deficient diet and can be cured by fresh fruit and vegetables, but the anti-scurvy factor, vitamin C (ascorbic acid), was only discovered in 1932. Citrus fruits, Brussels sprouts, black currants, tomatoes and cabbage are good sources. Human milk (but not cow's milk) is another source, but there is no vitamin C in meat. It is destroyed by cooking, and so it is usually absent in preserved or canned foods.

Vitamin C is essential for the formation and repair of the connective tissue and the ground substance that surrounds cells, as well as for the repair of capillary blood vessels. Deficiency is a result of inadequate intake, an unbalanced diet, or both. It often occurs in old people who live alone and sometimes in babies who are fed on heated cow's milk without fruit juice supplements. Because capillary walls are affected, patients with scurvy bruise readily and their gums bleed and swell. Skin wounds heal slowly. In infants, bleeding may occur into the intestines and around bones, and the bones themselves grow slowly because of lack of cement substance.

Vitamins D, E and K

Vitamin D is found in eggs, butter, milk, fish and fish liver oil, but not in vegetables. It is a lipid (fatty) substance related to cholesterol, and one variety of the vitamin is formed in the skin by the action of sunlight on 7-dehydrocholesterol.

Its action is to increase the absorption of calcium and phosphate from the intestines, and it is essential for the laying down of calcium bone. Its deficiency causes rickets; this may occur if the diet is inadequate, and in city dwellers who are cut off from bright ultraviolet light. The effects in children are a result of an insufficient calcium supply to growing bones. Growth is stunted and weight-bearing parts of the skeleton like the legs and spine become curved. Teeth develop badly and there may be muscular weakness. Today rickets is prevented by free school milk and adequate basic nutrition. Ultraviolet light and cod liver oil provide further supplies of vitamin D.

Vitamin E, which prevents abortion in rats, has no such obvious effect on humans. Vitamin K is needed for prothrombin formation (see page 117). Small quantities are present in many foods, and deficiency results not from inadequate diet but from disease of the liver, biliary system and intestines.

(*Left*) X-ray of a case of rickets. (*Right*) Child with rickets

(*Left*) The urinary system. The adrenal glands are not part of this system but are attached to the kidneys. (*Below*) Section through a kidney

Adrenal gland

Kidney

Vein

Artery

Ureter

Bladder

Urethra

Cortex

Medulla

Renal pelvis

THE URINARY SYSTEM

The anatomy of the urinary tract

The kidneys are on the back wall of the abdomen, just below the diaphragm and on either side of the vertebral column. Each one weighs about five ounces. It is supplied with blood by a single artery which comes from the aorta and divides into three branches. These branches are accompanied by veins which join to form the renal vein. The renal vein drains blood into the inferior vena cava.

Urine is formed in the substance of the kidneys and collects in the thin-walled, funnel-like renal pelvis. This leads into the ureter, the muscular wall of which contracts in slow waves, thereby helping the urine along to the bladder. Here urine is stored—a pint or so can be held with ease. In urination the tight sphincter at the base of the bladder relaxes and the smooth muscle wall of the bladder contracts. Although this action is really involuntary, it is well controlled by the cerebral cortex.

In cross-section, the kidney is composed of an outer cortex and an inner medulla. The cortex contains many thousands of tiny glomeruli; together with the renal tubules, which partly lie in the medulla, they make up the *nephrons* or functional units of the kidney.

Glomeruli are small knots of capillaries, derived from the finest branches of the renal artery. These knots are encased by Bowman's capsule, which is the bulbous ending of the cell-lined tubule. After a short twisted course, the tubule passes down into the medulla toward the renal pelvis and then doubles up on itself, travels up to the cortex where it twists again before its final downward passage to join the collecting system terminating in the renal pelvis.

Artery

Glomerulus

Vein

Capillary

Tubule

Collecting tubule

Urine to ureter

The excretory unit of the human kidney. Thousands of these units make up each kidney.

The functions of the kidneys

The major function of the kidneys is the removal of waste products, with the formation of urine. This is achieved while controlling the amount of salt and water in the body and maintaining the slight alkalinity of body fluids.

Cell metabolism produces various by-products which might be lethal if they were allowed to accumulate in the tissues. They are removed by the nephrons, which act as filters. From the blood in the glomeruli, fluid oozes into Bowman's capsule. Blood cells and large protein molecules remain in the capillaries because the pores in the 'filter' are too small to let them out. The filtered fluid then passes through the first downward part of the tubule, where 80 percent of the water and sodium in it is reabsorbed by the lining cells, and travels up into the cortex again. Here, under the influence of the hormone aldosterone, the remaining sodium is removed from it, and

(*Top*) When urine is allowed to dry, crystals of waste products will be seen. Not all of those shown here would be seen at the same time. (*Below*) Composition of urine

Water 95%

Urea 2%

Sodium chloride 1%

Other substances 2%
Creatinine; urates and uric acid; salts of calcium, magnesium, potassium and ammonia; pigments, etc.

78

Back to vein

From artery

The principle of the artificial kidney

Pump

Pump

Filter solution

hydrogen ions are excreted in exchange by the lining cells. The acidic liquid thus produced travels into the collecting ducts, the cells of which, stimulated by antidiuretic hormone, take up almost all the water that is left. Urine, now acidic and highly concentrated, drains into the renal pelvis and passes via the ureter to the bladder.

Receiving a fifth of the blood supply of the body, the kidneys filter off through their glomeruli 120 milliliters of fluid every minute. Only 1 milliliter of this becomes urine. In fact, just the minimum quantity needed to dissolve waste products is allowed to escape from the body.

Kidney damage and the artificial kidney

The kidneys are very susceptible to lack of oxygen or a severe fall in blood pressure, which can stop them functioning and damage their cells. Renal failure may also occur more gradually in diseases that affect the glomeruli and tubules. Whatever the cause, the effect is the same—toxic and acid waste products build up in the blood, and the patient dies unless treated. Kidney transplantation is possible in some cases; in others the artificial kidney is used. This works basically by osmosis—impurities in the blood are filtered off by passing the blood through a coiled tube immersed in a bath of clean fluid. The tube is a semipermeable membrane, allowing soluble substances of small molecular size to pass out while keeping in larger molecules.

Body fluids and electrolytes

The main constituent of the human body is water, which accounts for nearly two-thirds of the total body weight. An adult man of 155 pounds therefore contains about 12 gallons of water (a woman of the same weight would contain less as she has a greater amount of fat). Of this volume, about eight gallons is within the cells, maintaining their size and shape and acting as a vehicle for movement of salts, glucose, oxygen and the products of metabolism. About three gallons of water circulate in the heart and blood vessels. (The total blood supply, including red and white cells, is about five quarts.) The remaining three gallons of water is extracellular, and lies in the space between cells. The ability of the kidneys to retain the water of the body is obviously very important, for if all the

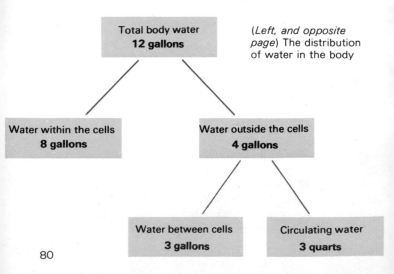

(*Left, and opposite page*) The distribution of water in the body

Total body water
12 gallons

Water within the cells
8 gallons

Water outside the cells
4 gallons

Water between cells
3 gallons

Circulating water
3 quarts

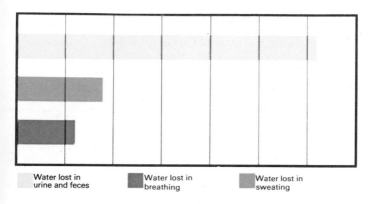

Water lost in urine and feces

Water lost in breathing

Water lost in sweating

fluid filtered by the glomeruli were to be excreted, the plasma volume would be lost within half an hour.

The salts dissolved in the body fluids — the electrolytes — are in the form of ions. Sodium, chloride, bicarbonate, potassium, calcium and phospate are the ions present in greatest quantity. An important fact is that while outside the cells sodium is found in high concentration and potassium in low concentration, the reverse holds true inside the cells. Potentially there is free movement of different ions in and out of cells, at a rate which depends on their relative concentration in two sites. The distribution of sodium and potassium in the body is thus the result of active physico-chemical processes; these two ions are segregated by the cell membranes, and this segregation is vital for cell function.

3 quarts

3 gallons

8 gallons

HORMONES AND REPRODUCTION

Some glands, such as those of the skin and the gastrointestinal tract, produce secretions which drain onto the surface or into a body cavity and have an effect only near where they are released. These are called *exocrine* (*exo*   outside). In contrast, the *endocrine* glands (*endo*   inside) manufacture substances which pass directly into the bloodstream, circulate all over the body and act at places far from where they originate. Such substances are *hormones;* at present nearly 30 are recognized, the products of eight different glands. They are mostly fairly simple organic chemical compounds and some have been made in the laboratory from artificial ingredients. They are effective in very small amounts and are the regulators of body processes, controlling growth and development, sexual activity, pregnancy and birth, and metabolism. Only in this century had hormone action begun to be understood, though before this the effects of damage to one or other of the endocrine glands were known—removal of the testes resulting in the excessive fat and sexual impairment of a eunuch; damage to the pancreas producing diabetes; shrinkage of the adrenals causing Addison's disease; and so on.

Regulation of body processes depends on regulation of hormone production. A few of the endocrine glands control themselves, but for the most part hormone secretion is under the control of the pituitary, a bean-shaped gland lying in a little cavity in the center of the base of the skull. The front or anterior part secretes a number of substances which go out in the blood to other glands and stimulate hormone formation; these hormones then circulate around to the pituitary and, if too much has been formed, suppress the stimulator—there is thus a sort of feedback system. The adrenal cortex, thyroid and sex organs are dependent on the pituitary. If this is damaged. these glands shrink and are unable to function.

The pituitary gland

Under the microscope the *anterior pituitary* is seen to be made up of nests of cells separated by blood vessels and connective tissue. The cells are of three sorts: *acidophil* (taking up, and thus stained by acid dyes), *basophil* (stained by basic dyes)

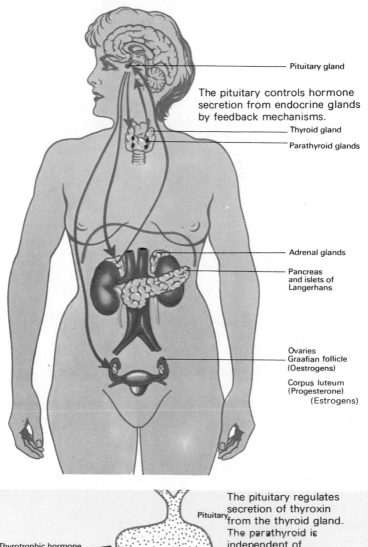

Pituitary gland

The pituitary controls hormone secretion from endocrine glands by feedback mechanisms.

Thyroid gland

Parathyroid glands

Adrenal glands

Pancreas and islets of Langerhans

Ovaries
Graafian follicle (Oestrogens)

Corpus luteum (Progesterone) (Estrogens)

The pituitary regulates secretion of thyroxin from the thyroid gland. The parathyroid is independent of pituitary control.

Pituitary

Thyrotrophic hormone

Thyroxin

Thyroid gland

Parathyroid hormone

Body cells

83

and *chromophobe* (without special affinity for dyes). Usually these stain red, blue and gray, respectively. The acidophil cells produce growth hormone and also a hormone which stimulates milk production in pregnancy. The basophils secrete hormones which stimulate the thyroid, adrenal cortex, ovaries and testes. Some chromophobes secrete hormones while some are probably inactive forms of the other cell types.

With pituitary tumors, excess growth hormone may be manufactured. If this occurs before puberty, there is gigantism because the bones are still able to elongate; after adolescence the growing ends of the bones (the epiphyses) are inactive, and the hormone causes the bones to get thicker and the soft tissues of the body to enlarge. A disease called acromegaly is the result. Insufficient growth hormone may be produced in pituitary disease, and some dwarfs are so because of this occurring before adolescence. In adults pituitary damage from any cause is likely to result in depletion of all hormones, leading to loss of weight and depression of thyroid, adrenal and sex functions. Occasionally pituitary damage is due to pressure

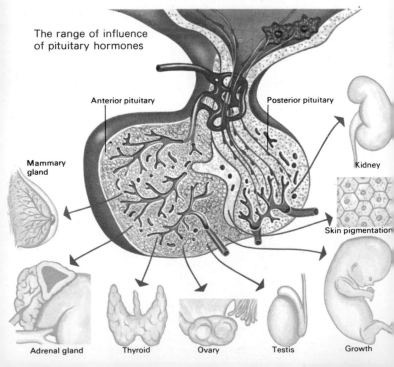

The range of influence
of pituitary hormones

Anterior pituitary

Posterior pituitary

Mammary
gland

Kidney

Skin pigmentation

Adrenal gland   Thyroid   Ovary   Testis   Growth

from a tumor of the basophil cells, with increased production of ACTH (*andrinocorticotropic hormone,* which stimulates the adrenal cortex) and signs of adrenal overactivity.

The *posterior pituitary* is really an extension of the brain, unlike the anterior part which is derived from the palate of the embryo. It contains nerve fibers, connective tissue and blood vessels. Its hormones are produced in the adjoining hypothalamas and are passed along nerve fibers in the stalk of the gland to be stored in the pituitary. There are two, *antidiuretic hormone* (ADH) and *oxytocin.* As noted on pages 78–79, ADH stimulates the kidney tubules to reabsorb water from the urine, and in damage of the posterior pituitary, *diabetes insipidus* results (insipid—as distinct from *mellitus,* sweet). In this condition 15 times the normal urine volume, or more than 30 pints a day, may be produced; the patient has to drink water by the bucketful to keep up with his kidneys.

Oxytocin causes contraction of the muscles of the viscera and thus helps the uterus to function in childbirth. It also causes ejection of milk from the breast in suckling.

Microscopic section of the anterior pituitary

Chromophobe cell

Basophil cell

Acidophil cell

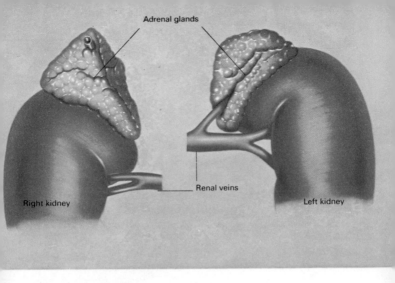

The adrenal glands lie at the upper end of the kidneys

The adrenal glands

Like the pituitary, the adrenal gland is a double organ, with two distinct and separately functioning parts—the outer *cortex* and inner *medulla*. There are two adrenals, yellow-brown triangular glands lying close to the upper end of the kidneys alongside the spine, and together they weigh about ¼ ounce. Like all endocrine glands, they have a rich blood supply. A microscope section shows that the cortex is made up of lightly staining cells containing much fat, arranged in three zones. Outside is a zone where the cells are in rounded groups, and beneath this there is a layer of cell columns running at right angles to the surface and an innermost irregular layer.

The *adrenal medulla* contains columns of large cells that manufacture *adrenalin* and *noradrenalin,* the two hormones that produce the effects of the *sympathetic nervous system.* There are cells of this system in the hypothalamus and spinal cord and in a chain running alongside the vertebrae, and its nerves go to the heart, blood vessels, intestines, bladder and wherever else there is smooth muscle, releasing noradrenalin at their endings. This hormone causes quickening of the pulse, increased blood pressure, constriction of blood vessels, decreased activity in bladder and bowel muscle, dilation of the pupil and a rise in blood sugar — preparing the body to react to a threat through 'flight or fight' behavior. Noradrenalin and adrenalin from the adrenals enter the blood to increase these actions. The effects of the two hormones differ in important ways, and they are probably produced by two different sorts of cells. Adrenalin had much stronger inhibitory actions (for example on the bladder and intestines), while noradrenalin is more powerful in raising the blood pressure and constricting arterioles.

When the sympathetic nervous system is active its effects are outwardly obvious, for the skin is pale (due to vasoconstriction) and there is gooseflesh (due to stimulation of the smooth muscle attached to the base of the hairs). There is also sweating, which however is produced not by adrenalin but by *acetylcholin*. This substance is involved in the transmission of nerve messages to voluntary muscle, but it also has effects on smooth muscle which are more or less opposite to those

Adrenal gland section (*left*) and 'flight or fight' reaction (*right*)

produced by the adrenal hormones. It is in fact the agent of the *parasympathetic nervous system* and is released from the parasympathetic nerve endings in smooth muscle all over the body.

The *adrenal cortex* forms a number of hormones which are essential to life. There are the *corticosteroids*; the two most important being *aldosterone* and *hydrocortisone*. Respectively they regulate the quantity of salt and water in the body, and control carbohydrate, protein and fat metabolism and help fight stressful conditions. Several other corticosteroids are produced in the adrenal, including cortisone, which is today synthesized and used in treatment.

The actions of aldosterone and hydrocortisone are clearly seen in states of adrenal under- or overactivity. *Addison's disease* is due to diminished adrenal function; patients with this condition suffer from weakness and tiredness, wasting (because of the lowering of blood sugar and lack of formation

Cushing's disease

Corticotrophin

Pituitary

Fall in blood corticosteroids

Rise in blood corticosteroids

Kidney

Salt and water metabolism

Liver

Carbohydrate metabolism

Production of corticosteroids

Testis

Ovary

Suprarenal gland

Sex functions

Adrenal cortex

Control and influence of the adrenal cortex

of new tissues), low blood pressure (because of lack of salt and water and decreased blood volume), loss of body hair, and sensitivity to stresses of various sorts. In addition they become pigmented, because pituitary ACTH secretion increases to try to make up for the low blood level of corticosteroids, and ACTH also stimulates the melanin-forming (pigment) cells of the skin. Increased cortical activity—often due to an adrenal tumor but occasionally seen with a pituitary tumor— produces *Cushing's disease.* Here the patient has thin limbs (because muscle protein is broken down to sugar), a fat trunk and rounded face (sugar is converted into fat), excessive hairiness (overproduction of male hormones), diabetes (high blood sugar, with insulin production inadequate to satisfy demands) and high blood pressure (excess aldosterone causing salt and water retention and increased blood volume).

Apart from cortisone, other corticosteroids have been synthesized, including some artificial ones which are more powerful than aldosterone and hydrocortisone. These include *prednisone,* which is used in inflammatory conditions, and *fluorocortisone,* which has a potent salt-retaining effect. Corticosteroids are also used to suppress immune reactions.

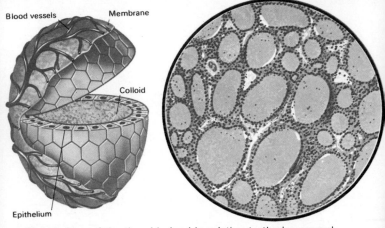

Blood vessels Membrane

Colloid

Epithelium

The position of the thyroid gland in relation to the larynx and
trachea is shown opposite. The structure of a follicle is shown
above (*left*) and a microscopic section through the thyroid gland
(*right*).

The thyroid gland

The thyroid is a fleshy pink-brown gland lying in the neck on
either side of the larynx and weighing about one ounce. Two
lobes are connected across the front by a narrow isthmus.
Thyroid tissue has a rich blood supply, several arteries enter-
ing its upper and lower parts. Four small *parathyroid glands,*
each about the size of a matchhead and yellowish-brown in
color, are loosely attached behind the upper and lower ends
of the thyroid, but sometimes the lower two are much farther
down and in the chest.

The surface of the thyroid is glistening and granular, for
the gland is made up of tiny spherical follicles containing a
jelly-like material. The epithelium of the follicles manufactures thyroid hormones which are then attached to protein and
stored as a gel. When the gland is hyperactive, the hormones are
released and the follicles collapse. An essential component of
these hormones is iodine, which must be present in the diet
in adequate amounts for the gland to function normally. Where
there is insufficient iodine—seafood is a good source of this
mineral—the gland enlarges in an attempt to compensate and
a goiter results, deforming the neck.

Epiglottis

Thyroid cartilage

Thyroid gland

Trachea
Parathyroid glands

The chief thyroid hormone is called *thyroxin*, and each molecule contains four atoms of iodine. Tri-iodothyronin has one atom less: it is produced in smaller quantity but is more powerful. The two hormones together stimulate metabolism and heat production, and if too much of them is produced this stimulation becomes excessive and the condition of thyrotoxicosis is obtained.

In *thyrotoxicosis,* a hyperthyroid state, which occurs most often in young women, the metabolic rate becomes very high. Carbohydrates, fats and proteins are needed in excess of normal; thus despite a good appetite and large food intake, the patient tends to lose weight. Subcutaneous tissue disappears and muscle bulk decreases. People with thyrotoxicosis feel hot and sweaty, with an overactive circulation and fast pulse. There is usually a slight but noticeable swelling of the thyroid gland and facial appearance is altered by the protrusion of the eyes. In young people the condition is treated by removing most of the over-functioning thyroid, but in older patients a dose of radioactive iodine is given — this is concentrated in the gland and the radioactivity kills the hormone-producing cells.

A minute quantity of radioactive iodine is used in the diagnosis of thyroid diseases. An overactive gland absorbs more than usual (and vice versa), and the amount concentrated in the gland can be measured.

Underactivity of the thyroid in the adult causes *myxoedema* and in infancy *cretinism*. Thyroxin is not only a metabolic stimulator but also an essential substance for body growth and the development of the brain. Cretins, who are thyroid deficient from birth, are stunted and severely retarded mentally. They have a coarse skin and features and a large tongue. Cretinism may result from iodine deficiency or from the absence of enzymes normally present in the thyroid. Treatment with thyroxin improves the general state but influences the mental condition only if it is started very early in life. In adults *myxoedema* is a condition in which patients are cold, slow physically and mentally, with a puffy face and swollen limbs and body, due to the laying down beneath the skin of a mucinous fluid. They feel excessively cold in winter, and as they lack the substances which stimulate metabolism they are

Myxoedema (*left*) and thyrotoxicosis (*right*)

One type of radioactive iodine scanner plots the iodine content of the thyroid in colors according to local concentration, from red (high) to blue (low).

prone to *hypothermia*, or marked lowering of body temperature, with severe consequences. Patients with myxoedema also tend to get anemia (thyroxin being essential for the normal formation of red blood cells) and heart disease, so diagnosis and treatment with thyroid hormones is vital.

An entirely different sort of hormone is made in the thyroid gland. This is *calcitonin*, which is secreted not by the follicular cells but by cells lying between the follicles and coming from a different source in the embryo. Its action is to lower the level of calcium in the blood, and it has thus the opposite effect to the parathyroid hormone.

The parathyroid glands

The parathyroids under the microscope can be seen to consist of cords of cells separated by wide blood spaces. There are two types of cells, most having a clear cytoplasm and a faint nucleus while a minority are red-staining with well-defined nuclei. The hormone secreted by these glands is called *parathormone,* and it stimulates the release of calcium from bone—by stimulating osteoclasts (bone cells)—while increasing the excretion of phosphate from the kidneys.

In the body, calcium and phosphate ions go hand in hand, an increase in one causing a reciprocal decrease in the other. Bone consists basically of a connective tissue scaffolding supporting a hard mass of mineral crystals, which are mainly calcium phosphate. When the parathyroid glands are overactive these crystals are removed from bone. Calcium and phosphate are poured into the bloodstream, but phosphate is selectively excreted in the urine, so that its level stays low. Some calcium is also lost from the kidneys, but the blood level remains high. As a result of the loss of calcium phosphate, the bones become soft and brittle. They may fracture with the smallest strain or they may twist and bend, as occurs in the condition called *osteitis fibrosa cystica.* Bone disease is not the

Microscopic section through a parathyroid gland

X-rays to show condition of osteitis fibrosa cystica (*left*) and appearance of normal limb (*right*)

only consequence of parathyroid overactivity, for the freed calcium in the blood is deposited in a variety of tissues, impairing their function. This is especially important in the kidneys, which may be severely involved; the pancreas is also sometimes affected, with painful inflammation.

Underproduction of parathormone has the opposite effect — a lowered blood calcium. This happens after the accidental removal of some of the parathyroid glands (a hazard of thyroid surgery), and its most important feature is tetany, or spontaneous prolonged twitching of muscles. Lowering the blood calcium level makes all the muscles abnormally excitable, so that the hands, feet and face may twitch distressingly. An injection of calcium cures this at once; administration of parathyroid extract has the same effect.

Diabetes and the islets of Langerhans

Scattered throughout the pancreas, between the glands that pour juice into the pancreatic duct, are many pinhead-sized groups of special cells. These are the islets of Langerhans and they secrete the hormone *insulin,* a deficiency of which is responsible for diabetes mellitus. With suitable stains, two types of islet cells can be demonstrated, each with characteristic granules. It is the beta cells which manufacture insulin and release it into the bloodstream.

A chemist's chart showing color coding for cartons of insulin, indicating the types and strengths available

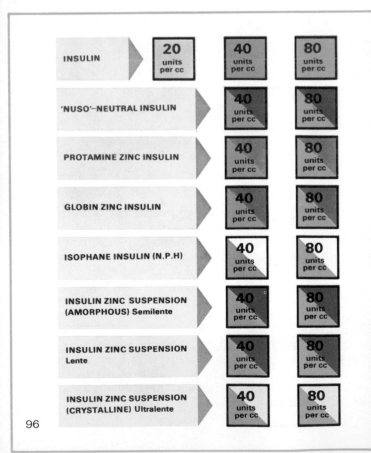

Insulin is a protein and its chief effect is to produce a lowering of the amount of glucose ('sugar') in the blood. It does this in several ways—by increasing the glycogen stores in the liver and the muscles, by hastening the entry of glucose into the cells and stimulating its breakdown into water and carbon dioxide and by promoting fat deposition. If insulin is deficient, the whole metabolism of the body suffers, though the immediate and obvious effect is an increase of blood glucose, which appears in the urine (hence diabetes *mellitus* —sweet). Insulin lack also causes an excessive breakdown of fats, so that strongly smelling ketones are produced. By osmotic action, the glucose in the urine takes with it a lot of water and also salts, and so someone with severe diabetes is thin and dehydrated, with ketones on his breath and sugar in his urine, and will go into coma and die unless treated. Before insulin was isolated about 50 years ago, this disease was always fatal. Now it is fairly easily controlled, the patient injecting himself with the required dose of insulin. Different sorts of insulin with varying lengths of action are available, as well as tab-

Microscopic section of the pancreas

Connective tissue   Islet of Langerhans   Pancreatic acini   Alpha cell

Coma

Blindness

Heart disease

Kidney disease

Skin infection

lets containing substances which lower the blood sugar level—these, however, cannot replace insulin if the diabetes is at all severe. Some patients with mild diabetes can be controlled with tablets or with dietary carbohydrate restriction, but moderate or severe diabetes always needs insulin.

Diabetes entails not only a disturbance of metabolism but also structural changes in the kidneys, eyes, blood vessels and nerves. These can cause kidney failure, blindness and gangrene of the feet, but can be prevented by careful treatment and regular medical checks.

The alpha cells of the islets secrete a hormone called *glucagon*, which raises the blood-glucose level by stimulating the breakdown of liver glycogen. The function of glucagon in the body is uncertain, and of minor importance compared with insulin.

The thymus

The thymus has not yet been shown to secrete a hormone, but it nevertheless exerts a powerful influence on the whole body, especially in the early part of life. It is a fatty bilobed gland at the root of the neck and in the front of the chest. Its outer part contains millions of dividing lymphocytes (lymphatic white cells) while the inner zone contains primitive structures called *Hassall's corpuscles*. At birth it is fairly large. It continues to grow up to the time of adolescence, after which it shrinks. By middle age all that remains is a few strands of tissue.

The thymus is of the utmost importance in the body's defenses against infection, for in the first few weeks of life the lymphocytes produced in it migrate into the bloodstream and colonize lymph nodes all over the body. Lymphocytes manufacture antibodies and are vital for immunity. If the thymus of newborn animals is damaged, there is a marked stunting of growth, development is retarded and there is a great susceptibility to infections—due to a reduction of the number of lymphocytes and impairment of antibody formation. The reduced resistance to infection which is brought about by corticosteroid treatment is paralleled by a shrinkage of the thymus and lymphoid tissue generally. This will lead ultimately to a lowered capacity for antibody formation.

(*Opposite page*) Those parts of the body affected by an acute deficiency of insulin.
The position of the thymus in the neck (*far left*), its blood supply (*left*) and microscopic structure (*below*)

Human sex determination
Nucleus with sex chromatin

Determination of sex

Whether a being is male or female is determined at the time of conception. All human cells have 23 pairs of chromosomes, one of these pairs being the sex chromosome. In women the sex chromosomes are an identical pair (XX), but in men one of the two is smaller (XY). When reduction division (meiosis) occurs in the germ cells of the ovaries and testes, the pairs are split. Thus all ova will have 22 + X chromosomes, as will half the spermatozoa. But the other half will have 22 + Y, and when one of these unites with a 22 + X ovum a male embryo (XY) results.

Occasionally reduction division goes wrong, and instead of having XX or XY sex chromosomes the fertilized ovum may have an extra X or a deficient Y. In such cases, characteristics of both sexes may be present. Intermediate sexuality can also occur as a consequence of abnormal hormone production in early life (thus overactive adrenal glands may produce external male features in baby girls). In adults, male or female, secondary sex characteristics may be acquired inappropriately as a result of hormone therapy.

Germinal vesicle   Follicular fluid

Microscopic section of an ovarian follicle

The ovaries, ovulation and menstruation

The female equivalents of the testes lie inside the pelvis. The size of a bean, they are supported by ligaments and are touched by the fronded ends of the Fallopian tubes, the ducts for the passage of ova to the uterus. The ovaries are the source of female germ cells (ova) and the female hormones, estrogen and progesterone. Ova are produced from follicles. These are minute spherical structures, precursors of which are present from infancy, but which begin to mature only at puberty. While up to 400,000 precursors are present in childhood, only one a month matures between the onset of menstruation and the time of menopause—a total of perhaps 400.

The maturing ovarian follicle secretes *estrogen,* which enters the bloodstream. Release of the ovum from the follicle occurs in most women in the second week after a menstrual period. After release, the wall of the mature follicle thickens and its cells multiply, forming the *corpus luteum,* which manufactures *progesterone* as well as estrogen.

Fallopian tube

Uterine cavity

Uterus

Ovary

Section through female
reproductive organs

Cervix

Vagina

Cycle of hormone secretion during menstruation

Menstruation, the shedding of the glandular lining of the uterus, is the result of cyclical hormone secretion. Under the influence of estrogen (in the first part of the month, before ovulation) the lining thickens, its capillaries multiplying and glands enlarging. Then, when progesterone is also secreted, greater thickening occurs. Just before menstruation, the corpus luteum degenerates; the supply of hormones is cut off and the uterine lining starts to slough. This continues for a few days until another follicle is maturing and a new cycle begins.

Ovarian hormone production is under the control of the pituitary, which triggers sexual development at puberty. One pituitary hormone (follicle-stimulating hormone) is active in the first half of the cycle; increasing blood estrogen suppresses it and elicits secretion of luteinising hormone, which activates the corpus luteum.

Pregnancy

After ovulation the ovum passes along the Fallopian tube and into the uterus. Unless fertilized, it dies within two days. However, if intercourse has taken place during this time, or within two days before ovulation, there is a chance that it will encounter a spermatozoon. When this happens, the fertilized ovum divides and becomes implanted in the thick glandular lining of the uterus. A placenta soon forms in this lining and produces a hormone called *chorionic gonadotrophin*. This prevents the disappearance of the corpus luteum and indeed stimulates it to secrete more estrogen and progesterone. The build-up of hormones is responsible for many of the physical changes of pregnancy—enlargement of breasts and uterus, laying down of fat, and fluid accumulation.

The developing fertilized ovum is an embryo in its first eight weeks and a fetus thereafter. It is nourished by the placenta, in which exchange of foodstuffs and oxygen takes place between maternal and fetal blood. The placenta also enables the fetus to eliminate waste products.

The fertilized egg cell multiplies by division to form a hollow morula (*above*). Blood supply to the placenta (*right*) and to the fetus (*left*)

The testes

The testes are formed in the abdomen and descend into the scrotum before birth. In the adult they are about 1½ inches long and egg-shaped, and are enclosed in a tough fibrous coat. Under the microscope, they are found to be composed of many long, thin, coiled tubules separated by groups of interstitial cells. The tubules contain layers of germ cells, the innermost of which turn into *spermatozoa*.

The male hormone *testosterone* is the product of the interstitial cells. At puberty these are set into action by a pituitary hormone, and they continue to secrete throughout adult life. Testosterone is responsible for male secondary sex features—growth of the genitals; hair growth all over the body but especially on the pubis, face and armpits; muscle development;

Structure of the human spermatozoon (*top*) and microscopic section through a testis (*right*) showing meiotic division of seminiferous tubule cells

(*Opposite*) Longitudinal section of a testis (*left*) and through the male pelvic region (*right*)

enlargement of the larynx, causing the voice to change; and sperm formation.

Spermatozoa have a head, a middle piece and a tail. The head contains the nucleus. The middle piece encloses mitochondria and is the energy source. The 1/20 mm-long tail bends from side to side and propels the sperm forward at up to one inch per minute.

Seminal fluid contains many million spermatozoa. These account for only a small fraction of its volume, most of which is a spermatozoan-nourishing medium, rich in the sugar fructose. The bulk comes from the epididymis (which sits on the testis), the seminal vesicles and prostate gland (at the base of the bladder), and further small glands which empty into the urethra. The testis and epididymis communicate via the vas deferens with these other glands, and in intercourse the combined products are expelled. Among the events in intercourse are erection (distension with blood) of the penis and of external female genitalia; outpouring of vaginal and other secretions to lubricate entry of the penis into the vagina; and reflex contraction of the male urethra, causing ejaculation of semen.

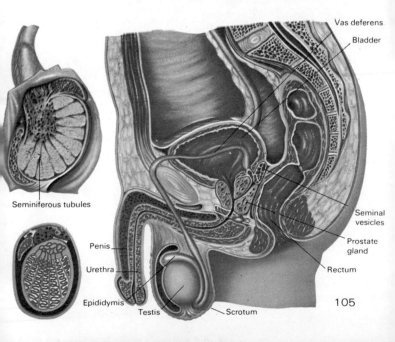

Vas deferens
Bladder
Seminiferous tubules
Seminal vesicles
Prostate gland
Penis
Urethra
Rectum
Epididymis
Testis
Scrotum

BLOOD

In the smallest organisms oxygen becomes available for vital functions through the process of diffusion; foodstuffs, after ingestion, are distributed in a similar way. Beyond a certain size, diffusion cannot meet the needs of the organism and oxygen and food transport is carried out by a specialized liquid tissue, the blood, which circulates within enclosed cavities. The chief function of the blood, the conveying of oxygen to the cells of the body, is indicated by its color, which is due to a pigment that can pick up oxygen and release it readily. In birds and mammals the pigment is hemoglobin, which contains iron. Not all species have red blood — some invertebrates, for instance, have blue blood containing a copper compound.

Not only does the blood carry oxygen to the tissues; it takes up the waste materials of cell metabolism (such as carbon dioxide and protein breakdown products) and carries them to the lungs and kidneys, where they are eliminated. It carries foodstuffs, minerals and hormones to the cells. Further-

Blood smears showing red cells and two white cells (*top*) and cluster of platelets (*below*)

Plan and side view of a red cell

more it protects the tissues of the body through its anti-infective components, the white cells and the plasma antibodies. When sealed in the vessels the blood is a stable tissue, and it responds to a breach of its confines by clotting, which is due to properties of the blood itself.

Clotting demonstrates that the blood is not just a simple solution of a dye, like red ink, but a composite fluid. A clot is derived mainly from the solid elements of the blood, which make up about 20 percent of its volume; the serum that oozes from a wound comes from the plasma, the liquid part of the blood. Under the microscope the solid elements are seen to be of three types: the *red cells* (the hemoglobin-containing, oxygen-carrying ones); the *white cells* (of various sorts, as shown by special stains, and involved in the response to infection); and the *platelets* (which take part in blood clotting). In every cubic mm of blood there are usually about 6 million red cells; between 5,000 and 10,000 white cells; and half a million platelets. The platelets are the smallest, only 1/400 mm in diameter; red cells are 1/140 mm across; white cells vary from 1/140 to 1/60 mm in diameter. Red cells are unusual in that they have no nucleus. They are concave on each side, giving a larger surface area for oxygen transport.

Mammals have five
types of white blood cell

Lymphocyte

Monocyte

Basophil

Neutrophil

Eosinophil

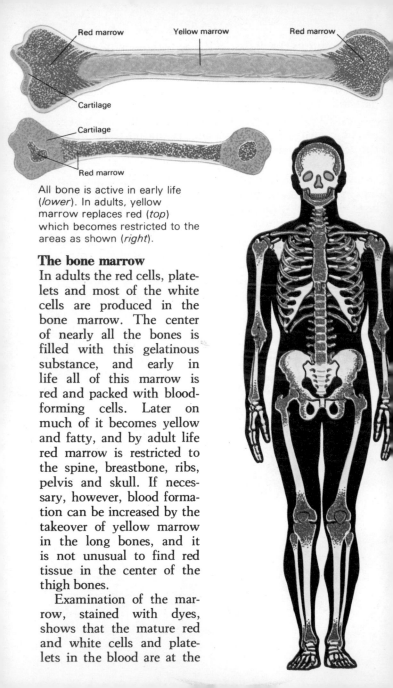

Red marrow   Yellow marrow   Red marrow

Cartilage

Cartilage

Red marrow

All bone is active in early life (*lower*). In adults, yellow marrow replaces red (*top*) which becomes restricted to the areas as shown (*right*).

The bone marrow

In adults the red cells, platelets and most of the white cells are produced in the bone marrow. The center of nearly all the bones is filled with this gelatinous substance, and early in life all of this marrow is red and packed with blood-forming cells. Later on much of it becomes yellow and fatty, and by adult life red marrow is restricted to the spine, breastbone, ribs, pelvis and skull. If necessary, however, blood formation can be increased by the takeover of yellow marrow in the long bones, and it is not unusual to find red tissue in the center of the thigh bones.

Examination of the marrow, stained with dyes, shows that the mature red and white cells and platelets in the blood are at the end of a line of ancestor cells. The most primitive precursor of the red corpuscle is the proerythroblast, which is up to 1/50 mm across and has a large nucleus and a blue-staining cytoplasm. This turns into the erythroblast and then the normoblast, which is smaller, has a smaller nucleus, and a pink-staining cytoplasm due to the formation of hemoglobin within it. The normoblast is the same size as a mature red cell, but differs from it in having a nucleus. This is then gotten rid of, producing the young red cell or reticulocyte which still has wisps of blue-staining in its cytoplasm.

The precursors of all the granular white cells and of some of the non-granular ones (lymphocytes and monocytes) are mingled in the marrow with red cell precursors. Myeloblasts turn into the smaller myelocytes, which have round nuclei and granules of various sorts, and then into white cells, whose nuclei are segmented like a string of sausages. Platelets are formed from large (1/25 mm) multinucleated cells, the megakaryocytes, which break up into little pieces. Another cell found in the marrow is the plasma cell, which makes antibodies which are released into the blood.

Human red bone marrow smear

Red cells, iron, B_{12} and anemia

The normal biconcave 1/140 mm red cell is filled with the iron-containing compound hemoglobin, which can combine reversibly with oxygen and carbon dioxide and is the basis of respiratory gas exchange. In 100 ml of blood there are normally about 14 grams of hemoglobin, and anemia exists where there is a smaller quantity. Whatever the cause, anemia can be measured by dissolving the red cells and examining the color of the resulting solution.

Iron deficiency is the commonest cause of anemia. In the body there is about 4.5 grams of iron, over half of which is in hemoglobin, and under normal conditions it is obtained from the diet and lost from the body in small amounts. If loss exceeds intake, hemoglobin will fall. This occurs with prolonged bleeding (as in the case of women with heavy periods) or if the diet is inadequate (as happens sometimes in old age). The anemic blood contains fewer cells than normal and they are paler and smaller than usual.

For the maturation of cells in the bone marrow, several hormones and dietary factors are essential. These include thyroxin, vitamin C, folic acid and vitamin B_{12}. Particularly

Hypochromic anemia in venous blood cells (*left*)
The smear shows pale cells due to insufficient hemoglobin.
The bone marrow smear (*right*) shows the effect of hemorrhage resulting in large numbers of red cell precursors.

if the last two are deficient, as happens when they are inadequately absorbed from the gastrointestinal tract, this maturation is delayed and the cells which are released from the marrow into the blood may be larger than usual and nucleated. Vitamin B_{12} is a deep red, cobalt-containing substance, found in meat, eggs and milk and normally absorbed from the small intestine. Very small amounts are required for health. In *pernicious anemia* the stomach lining is abnormal and absorption is impaired; anemia and nervous damage result.

Anemia also occurs when red cell production is less than red cell breakdown. These cells normally live for three to four months before being destroyed in the spleen and marrow. Destruction may be excessive in a variety of conditions in which there are abnormal forms of hemoglobin or abnormal enzymes in the cells, or in cases where the red cells are weakened by the presence of malarial parasites. In these states *hemolysis* occurs, and the released hemoglobin is converted into the bile pigment *bilirubin* which may enter the blood in sufficient quantity to produce obvious jaundice.

Polycythemia is 'too many red cells'. It happens when the marrow is stimulated excessively — often without clear cause — and leads to a purple-red complexion rather than a pallid one.

Pernicious anemia results in large, pale, red blood cells and many lobed nuclei in white cells (*left*). In bone marrow (*right*) large red cell precursors form.

111

Phagocytic white cells engulf bacteria at a skin wound (*top*)

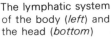

The lymphatic system of the body (*left*) and the head (*bottom*)

White cells and defense against infection

White cells are of two main types—those with and those without granules in their cytoplasm. The granular cells, which are formed in the marrow, are *phagocytic* and can engulf foreign matter (such as bacteria), and in the presence of tissue damage they are stimulated to activity. Inflammation is due to a localized increase of blood flow in the damaged area and a leakage of fluid and cells from capillary blood vessels. These are the reasons for the redness and swelling. Pus consists of many millions of granular white cells released from the blood to ingest bacteria or dead material, and its presence is the sign both of abnormal local conditions and of a normal body response.

Most of the non-granular cells are *lymphocytes*. These are made in the spleen and in the lymph nodes, which are found in chains all over the body but especially in close relation to the main blood vessels. The nodes contain areas of active cell production; lymphocytes pass from here into lymph channels which eventually drain into the superior vena cava and

Monocytes, which number a few percent of the white cells in the blood, resemble large lymphocytes but have an indented rather than a round nucleus. They are phagocytic and are the representatives in the blood of the *reticulo-endothelial system*, which comprises similar cells in the connective tissue (macrophages), liver (Kupffer cells), spleen and lymph nodes. These are all scavengers, removing damaged or dead cells and foreign particles, and then destroying or storing them.

Plasma and plasma proteins — immunization

The fluid part of the blood, the plasma, is a colorless solution containing proteins and smaller amounts of salts, glucose, amino acids and other substances. In normal plasma there are about 7.5 grams of protein per 100 ml compared with the equivalent of less than 1 gram of sodium chloride. The plasma proteins in terms of quantity are the most important plasma

(*Left*) Separation of plasma proteins by electrophoresis shows the relative proportions of each component. The gamma globulins are the antibodies involved in the immune response to disease and are more in evidence in the left-hand strip. (*Right*) Proportion of cells and plasma in blood

Diagrammatic structure of a lymph node

Afferent lymph vessel

Trabecula

Cortex

Lymph nodule

Reticulum

Efferent lymph vessel

Vein

Artery

the right atrium. Cells formed in the spleen go directly into the bloodstream. Besides these lymphocyte-producing tissues, there are several others containing large collections of lymphocytes. These include the tonsils and adenoids.

When exposed to foreign structures, like transplanted tissues or micro-organisms, lymphocytes multiply and make antibodies in an effort to neutralize the foreign matter. They are thus involved in the fight against infection and in the rejection process after transplant surgery.

Venous sinusoids

Penicillate artery with ellipsoid

Arterial plexus

Lymph nodule

Diagrammatic structure (*left*) of the spleen (*right*)

Splenic artery

Splenic vein

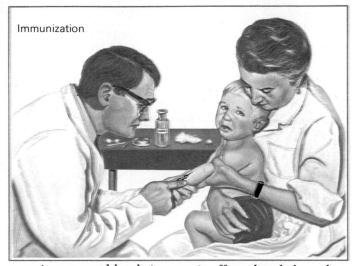

Immunization

constituents, and by their osmotic effect they help to keep fluid within the blood vessels and prevent it from accumulating in the tissues.

The different proteins can be separated in the laboratory by means of a process involving a powerful electric field (electrophoresis). About two-thirds of the protein is *albumin,* which is of relatively low molecular weight and is formed in large quantity in the liver. In starvation or in liver disease, much less is manufactured, and in some kidney diseases considerable amounts are lost in the urine: in these conditions the osmotic pressure of the blood falls and fluid leaks into the tissues, producing edema (swelling). Most of the remaining third of the plasma proteins is constituted by the *globulins.* Three main groups are recognized—*alpha, beta* and *gamma.* They have large molecules, gamma globulin being over twice the size of albumin, and they are synthesized by the cells of the reticuloendothelial system. New gamma globulin is formed as a result of infection, for it contains the specific antibodies against infecting agents. 'Active' immunization involves antibody production in response to a small dose of a bacterium or virus. The organism need not be alive; provided its antigenic components are not damaged, an inoculated dead organism is effective in eliciting an antibody response.

Plasma
(liquid
minus blood
cells)

Serum
(liquid
minus
clotting
elements)

Blood cells

Clot
(blood cells
enmeshed
in fibrin)

Erythrocytes

Platelets

Fibrin threads

Parents

Carrier

Y X ⟷ X x

Sex chromosomes

Bleeder   Carrier

Y X   Y X   X X   X x

Blood coagulation

Fibrinogen, another plasma protein, is present in blood in small amounts—about 0.3 grams per 100 ml. It is a vital substance for the clotting of blood, which results from the conversion of fibrinogen to fibrin. Fibrin forms masses of fibers that combine with enmeshed platelets and red and white cells to make up a clot. The defibrinated plasma is left as serum.

Platelets are very fragile. If vessel walls and tissues are damaged, as occurs whenever there is bleeding, they break up and release substances which react with a number of constituents of the blood and tissues to form thromboplastin. *Prothrombin* is yet another plasma protein, manufactured in the liver and present in the bloodstream in small quantities; in the presence of calcium salts, it is con-

If blood is prevented from clotting, cells separate out from plasma (*top left*). On clotting, a clear fluid (serum) remains (*top right*).

Microscopic section of a blood clot (*middle*) and hemophilia inheritance (*bottom*)

Substances involved in clotting (*opposite*)

verted by the newly produced thromboplastin into thrombin. This is the agent that actually induces clot formation, for it is a protein-destroying enzyme that digests part of the fibrinogen. The remaining fibrinogen then combines with itself to form the fibrin masses.

It follows that a number of different conditions can produce abnormal bleeding. If the capillaries are excessively fragile, as occurs in vitamin C deficiency, tiny spots of blood appear in the skin (purpura). If, in contrast, one of the major factors needed for clotting is deficient, large-scale bleeding may result. Thus in hemophilia one of the plasma components necessary for the formation of thromboplastin is present in much-reduced quantities, and so small cuts and bruises bleed uncontrollably. This disease occurs almost entirely in males; it is an hereditary condition transmitted on an abnormal X chromosome by females, in whom it is hidden due to the presence of the other, normal, X. A similar but milder disorder called Christmas disease is inherited in a different way. Excessive bleeding also happens when the platelets are deficient in number, as in severe disease of the bone marrow; in biliary disease and vitamin K deficiency, which produce a reduction in prothrombin levels in the blood; and in certain rare conditions in which fibrinogen is absent.

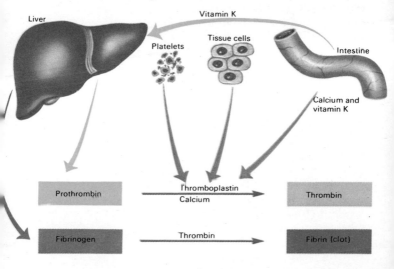

Blood groups and transfusion

Before the discovery of blood groups at the turn of the twentieth century, blood transfusion was a hit-or-miss procedure, sometimes successful but sometimes totally disastrous. We now know that immune reactions are responsible for 'incompatible' blood transfusions, for red cells possess certain antigens and plasma contains related antibodies. The presence of these is determined genetically; antibody is never present in the same blood as its related antigen, for if the two meet, the red cells mass together and then dissolve. This, however, is precisely what happens when incompatible blood is transfused—disaster may follow, because the damage to the red cells can lead to fatal shock and kidney damage.

There are two antigenic red cell substances, known as A and B. They are complex sugars. Red cells can be of four kinds—A, B, AB (containing both) and O (containing neither). In Western nations O and A are most common (46 percent and 42 percent of the population) while B (9 percent) and AB (3 percent) are rare. The serum of someone belonging to group O contains anti-

Fetal blood is incompatible with maternal blood in a Rhesus baby (*above*)

The effect of serum A and B on blood cells determines blood groups. Tests are carried out on glass slides (*opposite*).
Serum A, containing anti-B, agglutinates both B and AB cells. Transfusion of B or AB cells would therefore stimulate an anti-B reaction in a group A recipient; O cells, with no antigens, would not be reacted to.

bodies to A and B, while a person in group AB has neither antibody and someone in A or B has antibody only to the other. Before transfusion can be carried out, the cells of the donor and the recipient must be grouped against serum of known groups, while in addition the cells to be transfused must be tested directly with the recipient's serum.

The other major blood group system is the Rhesus system. The Rhesus 'factor', which is a collection of antigens, was first found in the red cells of Rhesus monkeys, but it is present in about 85 percent of humans (who are termed Rh+) and absent in about 15 percent (Rh−). Rhesus *antibodies* are not usually present in the plasma of this 15 percent. Like other blood group substances, the 'factor' is inherited, and its practical importance lies in the observation that the child of an Rh+ father and Rh− mother may itself be Rh+. If this occurs, the Rh+ cells of the fetus will set up the formation of antibodies in the mother's circulation. This process is cumulative, rarely affecting a first-born child; with subsequent children these antibodies can possibly enter their bloodstreams, destroying their red cells in the way already described. A Rhesus baby—severely jaundiced, anemic, premature and sometimes spastic—is the result. Its bone marrow makes up for red cell loss by releasing erythroblasts, but their quantity is inadequate and often the only way to save the baby is by transfusing healthy blood to replace the abnormal blood. Modern medicine has recently perfected a serum that negates any antibody build-up in the mother. Now subsequent babies face no greater danger than the first.

Group B serum

Group A serum

Group O   Group B   Group A   Group AB

Skull

Cerebrum

Cerebellum

Spinal cord

THE NERVOUS SYSTEM

The nervous system is made up of the brain, spinal cord and nerves. It has two basic functions — the detection and processing of information from within and outside the body and the production and control of movement through stimulation of muscle action. The brain is also the seat of consciousness, and the mind is in some way a reflection of its activity.

The adult brain weighs about three pounds. It contains the *cerebrum,* its longest region; the *brainstem,* which joins up with the spinal cord; and the *cerebellum,* which lies behind the brainstem below the cerebrum and is concerned with the fine control of movement. The surface of the cerebrum is wrinkled with convolutions separated by fissures; the wrinkling creates a large surface area, allowing many brain cells to be packed into a limited space. Groups of convolutions form several distinguishable lobes, each of which has a particular function. When the cerebrum is sliced, it is seen to consist of an outer gray layer, the *cerebral cortex,* beneath which is a mass of white tissue. Within the brain are four interlinked cavities, or *ventricles,* through which fluid circulates, acting as a shock absorber for delicate tissue. Around the ventricles in the cerebrum are several masses of gray matter known as the *basal ganglia.* They are gray and translucent like the cortex because they are full of nerve cells. White matter appears pale and opaque, in contrast, because it is made up of nerve fibers with fatty insulating sheaths.

The uppermost part of the brainstem, the *midbrain,* is tucked up into the cerebrum. It contains a number of movement-coordinating centers; it is also responsible for sleep and wakefulness. Beneath this is the *pons* (bridge), connecting with the cerebellum. Joining the pons to the spinal cord is the *medulla,* in which are groups of nerve cells regulating such vital functions as respiration and blood pressure. The surface of the cerebellum is finely folded into *folia* (leaves) that resemble the cerebral convolutions in having outer

(*Opposite*) The brain enclosed in the cranial cavity

Areas of the body supplied by the spinal nerves. The orange area is supplied from the cervical segments of the spine, the yellow area from the thoracic segments, the green area from the lumbar segments, and the pink area from the sacral segments.

(*Above*) Cell body of a motor neuron
(*Below left*) A nerve impulse crosses a synapse by causing release of a chemical transmitter stored in the synaptic vesicles. The transmitter generates a new impulse on the other side of the cleft.
(*Below right*) Diagram of motor neuron showing route of nerve impulse.

gray and inner white layers.

The spinal cord runs from the base of the skull to the level of the upper lumbar spine. While the brain itself gives off 12 pairs of nerves, serving sensation and movement in the head and neck, the cord gives off 31 pairs supplying the trunk and limbs. An H-shaped core of gray nerve cells forms a column in the center of the cord, surrounded by white nerve fibers. The front prongs of the H contain cells responsible for movement, while the back prongs are involved in sensation. The white matter contains ascending sensory pathways to the brain and descending motor pathways. Each spinal nerve is made of two nerve roots, motor and sensory, which emerge from the front and back of the cord and join together.

Impulse

Mitochondrion

Synaptic vesicles

Synaptic cleft

Dendrite or cell body

Nissl granules   Synaptic knob   Dendrite

Cell body   Nucleus

Neurons and nerve fibers

The structural and functional unit of the nervous system is the nerve cell or *neuron;* nervous tissue is composed of neurons, their elongated outgrowths, and a form of connective tissue known as *neuroglia.* Neurons are electrically charged cells which, once formed, cannot be renewed or replaced. They give off long extensions which constitute nerve fibers and may be three feet or more in length. These specialized structures, in continuity with the body of the cell, conduct nerve impulses (which are electrical waves) at high speed and in so doing carry messages within, to, and from the brain.

Neurons in different parts of the brain and cord vary widely in size and shape. The granule cells in the cortex of the cerebellum are only 1/200 mm in diameter while the big motor cells in the spinal cord reach 1/8 mm across. However, virtually all types are composed of a cell body, an *axon,* which arises from the axon hillock of the cell and may run a considerable distance as a nerve fiber and *dendrites,* which are finely branching protoplasmic processes.

The cell body can be stained to show Nissl granules, which disappear when the cell is damaged or is repairing itself. Axons are fine cylinders which convey information to or from the cell body and, in the brain, end by branching to meet the dendrites of other nerve cells at junctions called synapses. Learning, memory and information storage within the brain involve not only biochemical changes in the nerve cells but also the forming of new synapses. Dendrites (absent in some

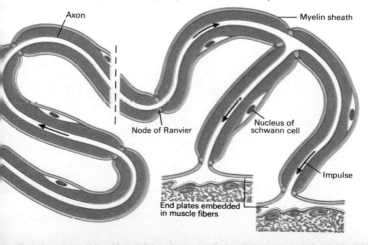

Axon

Myelin sheath

Node of Ranvier

Nucleus of schwann cell

Impulse

End plates embedded in muscle fibers

specialized receptor cells concerned with vision, balance and hearing) may connect the parent cell with the axons of many other neurons and thus act as a vast receptor area for messages.

Neuroglia and Schwann cells

The neuroglia, the supporting elements, are of three main types—*astrocytes, oligodendrocytes* and *microglia*. They fill up the space between the neuronal structures and are important in the maintenance of nerve function. *Astrocytes* are the largest, and are star-shaped cells with branching processes. They are found chiefly in the gray matter and are involved in the nutrition of neurons and the repair of brain damage.

Oligidendrocytes are smaller and have fewer branches. In white matter they lie singly or in rows between nerve fibers, the fatty insulated coverings of which they produce. *Microglia* are the smallest of the glial cells and are scattered throughout the brain. They are the scavengers; they may pick up remnants of damaged cells and move around.

Two special types of neuroglia occur in the ventricles

The progressive development of a myelin sheath is illustrated above. The drawing below shows a couple of myelinated nerves.

Astrocytes   Microglia   Oligodendrocyte

The three types of neuroglia cell

of the brain. The *ependyma* is the ciliated (hair-like) border covering the layer of columnar cells that serve as the lining of the central cavities of the brain and spinal cord. The *choroid plexuses,* which produce cerebrospinal fluid, are gland-like folded masses of similar, flatter cells.

The nerve fibers which exit from the brain and cord make up the nerves of the head, trunk and limbs. They are of two sorts — those with and those without a fatty covering known as the *myelin sheath.* In peripheral nerves myelin is formed by *Schwann cells,* which envelop the nerve axons and cover them with layer upon layer of protein and fat. This myelin sheath acts as an electrical insulator and enables nerve messages to be conducted faster; the thicker axons, which are faster conductors than thinner ones, are myelinated, while small-diameter axons are without such a sheath. Myelin is laid down in segments, which may be several millimeters long. Each segment is produced by one Schwann cell, and the junction between two is at the structure called the *node of Ranvier.*

The detailed structure of a node of Ranvier

Crenated myelin — Schwann cell cytoplasm — Axon — Mitochondria — Gap substance — Basement membrane — Fluted axon — Myelin — Myelin sheath

Muscle

Fiber

Fibril

Electron micrograph
of fibril

I A H A I

Biceps

Triceps

Flexion

Extension

Pairs of antagonistic
muscles alternately
contract and relax to
produce opposing
movements. A muscle
is built up from fibrils
aligned together.

Skeletal muscle

The muscles of the head, trunk and limbs are known as
voluntary muscles, for they contract and produce movements
in response to conscious efforts of will. They are also called
striped muscles, for under the microscope their long thin
fibers are seen to have fine dark and light cross-markings.
These are the A band and the I band, and they contain two
proteins, respectively *myosin* and *actin.* The two form a
complex substance, *actomyosin;* its molecules are able to
contract in response to nervous messages. This is the basis of
movement. Actomyosin can be extracted from muscles and
under special conditions converted into threads which
shorten in the presence of the compound ATP (*adenosine triphosphate*), providing a demonstration model of
muscular contraction. The energy for contraction comes
from glucose, itself derived from glycogen stores in muscle.
Lactic acid is formed as a by-product. This accumulates
in muscles that are used heavily or deprived of adequate

blood flow, and an excess amount causes cramp.

Muscles make up the bulk of soft tissue in a well-nourished person, and are familiar as red meat. How is it that an infinite variety of movements can be produced by structures that are anchored at both ends and can merely contract and relax? The answer lies in the complexity of the muscle arrangement in the body and the fact that for every muscle there is another which has the opposite action—its antagonist. This enables every movement to be controlled in force and range, while the intricate arrangements of muscles across joints allow the greatest possible diversity of action. An example of antagonism is provided by the biceps and triceps. The biceps is attached by tendons above to the shoulder joint and the humerus and below to the radius. When it contracts, the forearm is brought closer to the shoulder. The triceps runs from the top of the humerus across the elbow joint to the upper end of the ulna, and its contraction therefore straightens the elbow and the whole arm. When the biceps is in action, the triceps is relaxed, and vice versa.

The body contains a large number of separate muscles in a complex arrangement.

Changes in electrical potential and movement of ions across the nerve membrane during an action potential

Voluntary movement

Willed movements begin as electrical activity in large neurons of the cerebral cortex. Nerve impulses send messages from these cells along myelin-enclosed nerve fibers to the motor neurons of the spinal cord. The axons of these cells constitute motor nerve fibers which convey impulses to muscle. The nerve messages arrive at special neuromuscular junctions and induce contraction of the muscle fibers.

The changes that occur in nerves and muscles during such activity are both electrical and chemical in nature. In the resting state, there are many potassium ions and few sodium ions inside the nerve cell and axon and little potassium and much sodium outside the nerve cell. These concentration differences are due to properties of the thin cell membrane surrounding each neuron and its nerve fiber. This membrane is also responsible for the electrical charge of the nerve cell (about 60 millivolts, the inside of the cell being negative in relation to the outside). Nerve cell activity and nerve impulses consist basically of very brief changes of electrical

Local current flow during passage of action potential.

The impulse invades the axon terminals.

Myelin sheath

Axon

Muscle fibrils

charge and ionic concentration. The electrical change is the *action potential*, a spike of positive voltage lasting a few thousandths of a second, and this is associated with a brief reversal of the normal distribution of sodium and potassium. The nerve impulse is formed by the passage of the action potential along the axon at speeds up to 200 feet per second. In the faster-conducting myelinated fibers these electrical and chemical events are confined to the nodes of Ranvier, enabling a very rapid stepwise transmission of the impulse to occur.

On arriving at the neuromuscular junction, the nerve impulse releases from the nerve endings a minute quantity of the compound *acetylcholine*, which passes across to the muscle, becomes attached to special sites and causes rapid changes in electrical charge and ionic concentrations like those in conducting nerve tissue. The changes continue throughout the muscle fibers and initiate contraction. Acetylcholine lasts only for a short while, and is rapidly destroyed by the enzyme cholinesterase. Curare (the South American blowpipe arrow poison) paralyzes by becoming attached at the neuromuscular junction and so blocking the normal action of acetylcholine.

A tracing of the tension developed in a single muscle twitch

Latent period

Contraction phase

Relaxation phase

Stimulation

0·01 sec

0·04 sec

0·05 sec

129

Heat

Touch

Light touch air currents

Cold

Pressure

Pain

The receptor nerve endings in the skin subserving different
sensations have different structures although they are all basically
dendrites of sensory neurons.

Sensation and sensory receptors

In addition to the special senses—sight, hearing, taste and
smell—the body possesses the means of detecting and inter-
preting a wide variety of sensations arising from both within
and without and affecting the skin, viscera, muscles, joints
and tendons. These sensations include touch, pressure, pain,
vibration, heat and cold, and the positioning of parts of the
body, and they come about through the effect of external and
internal stimuli on sensory receptor organs. Stimuli may be
mechanical or (in the case of extremes of pain and temperature)
physico-chemical, but the result is the same, the receptor
sending messages in the form of nerve action potentials to the

central nervous system. Sensory receptors are thus *transducers* and can be compared with microphones or record player cartridges, which convert a mechanical input into an electrical output.

The sensory receptors of the body show widely varied structure under the microscope. Structure is related to function, and the simplest receptors, which are merely nerve endings in the skin, are responsible for detecting pain, while complex basket-like or onion-shaped receptors respond to light touch, small movements and pressure. All, however, are

Impulses from receptors in the skin pass through the spinal cord to the brain. Some axons pass right up the cord before synapsing in the medulla; others synapse upon entry into the spinal cord.

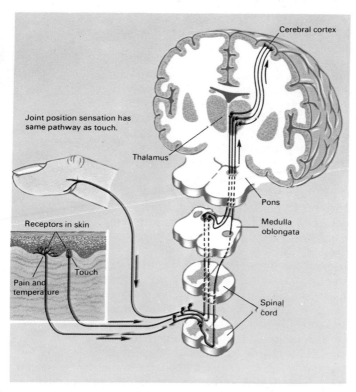

the endings of sensory nerves, and the information they send is in the form of nerve impulses. As the nerve action potential is constant in size and duration, change in input is signaled to the brain as a change in the frequency of impulses.

Sensory messages in sensory nerves enter the central nervous system in the posterior roots of the spinal cord. These nerves are the extensions of nerve cells lying in a small swelling (ganglion) of the posterior root, and the centrally traveling processes of the same cells carry the messages into the cord, through which they eventually reach the cerebral cortex. In the cord the first sensory fibers may transmit their information to other cells, and between the cord and the cerebrum are relay stations, which analyze the messages received.

Reflex activity —
the organization of the spinal cord

Reflexes are unconscious actions in response to sensory stimuli. The withdrawal of a hand from something very hot that has been touched inadvertently and the kick produced by a sharp tap on the tendon just below the kneecap are both reflex actions. These and all the many other reflexes are mechanisms of the central nervous system, having in common an incoming sensory and outgoing motor pathway. They are inborn and involuntary actions, and the spinal cord and brainstem are responsible for most of them, so that they may still be present even after a great deal of brain damage has occurred. 'Conditioned reflexes', which are acquired responses based on these actions, are different because they involve the cerebral cortex and cannot be established in its absence.

In the simplest reflex, the knee jerk, the tap below the kneecap briefly stretches the tendon, stimulating stretch receptors in it. These receptors send off a volley of nerve impulses to the spinal cord. The incoming message is carried directly to the motor neuron in the anterior horn of the cord; the motor neuron then fires off a set of impulses which travel along its axon and reach the muscle at the front of the thigh. This muscle contracts, straightening the leg and thus combating the original stretch to the muscle and its tendon. Hence the reflex has a *protective* function, preventing damage to the muscle. Similarly, all other reflexes either prevent injury or help to restore the normal state of the body.

The knee jerk must, in fact, be far more complex than the simple description just given because for maximum efficiency, contraction of a muscle is accompanied by relaxation of its antagonist. In this case the hamstring muscles at the back of the thigh relax while the others contract, and this relaxation is produced reflexively by suppression of the activity of the hamstring motor nerve cells. This suppression occurs through the agency of intermediate neurons in the cord, for the incoming sensory impulses from the stretched tendon are also relayed up the spinal cord along a number of pathways.

In a spinal reflex, information from receptors is channeled to motor neurons innervating appropriate muscles without passing through centers in the brain. With the knee jerk there is only one synapse between the sensory neuron and the motor neuron. Usually there are intervening neurons to relay the information.

The control of movement

Normally muscular movements are smooth and coordinated because of reflex activity, nervous feedback (servo) systems, and the mass of ever-changing information impinging on the spinal motor neurons. If the normal working of the brain and spinal cord is disturbed, movements may become weak, stiff or jerky and complicated actions like walking may become impossible.

Movements begin as electrical activity of the *pyramidal cells* of the motor area of the cerebral cortex, which lies just in front of the central furrow. From these cells the fibers pass downward and are grouped together in the internal capsule deep in the brain. They then descend in front of the midbrain as the

Impulses from the cortex impinge on spinal motor neurons directly via the pyramidal tract (*above*), but contraction is also controlled indirectly and from the cerebellum via the gamma pathway (*below*).

The cerebellum in
relation to other brain
structures
Insert shows Purkinje
cells of cerebellum

cerebral peduncles. Lower, in the *medulla,* the two groups of
fibers cross each other and pass down into the spinal cord,
terminating at the motor neurons. This crossing over explains
why in strokes the damage is in one half of the brain while
the paralysis is on the other side of the body.

The corticospinal motor fibers carry messages which set off
voluntary movements by activating spinal motor neurons.
These cells are influenced also by impulses from the basal ganglia, midbrain reticular formation, pons and cerebellum, which
regulate their activity; they are moreover affected reflexively by
the muscles themselves. Muscles are in a state of tension
('tone') due to occasional contraction of groups of their fibers.
Tone is determined by a small number of special fibers that contract slightly in response to impulses from small ('gamma')
motor neurons. Tension receptors around these fibers then fire
off and their messages, arriving at the spinal cord, activate the
larger ('alpha') motor neurons supplying the rest of the muscle.
When the tension in the muscle as a whole is the same as that in
the special fibers, motor neuron activity stops temporarily.

135

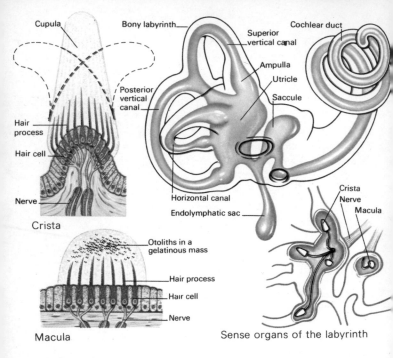

Labels in figure:
Cupula
Bony labyrinth
Superior vertical canal
Cochlear duct
Ampulla
Utricle
Saccule
Posterior vertical canal
Hair process
Hair cell
Nerve
Crista
Horizontal canal
Endolymphatic sac
Crista
Nerve
Macula
Otoliths in a gelatinous mass
Hair process
Hair cell
Nerve
Macula

Sense organs of the labyrinth

Balance, the cerebellum and the labyrinths

The cerebellum is important in the regulation of movement and in maintaining balance, in which it works in close connection with the balance organs or *labyrinths*. Each cerebellar hemisphere is linked to a labyrinth, to the opposite half of the cerebrum, and to the spinal cord on the same side. This spinal connection means that damage to the cerebellum causes disturbances of movement such as clumsiness and tremors on the same side of the body as the damage (in contrast to cerebral damage). Fibers from the cerebellum also activate the 'gamma' motor neurons of the cord, and so in cerebellar disease muscular tone is diminished and the muscles may become very lax.

The labyrinths, one on each side, are situated in the inner ear, deep in the sides of the skull. Through their linkages with the cerebellum, brainstem and cerebral cortex they continually influence the motor activity of the spinal cord. They pick up information about the position of the head and analyze it so that messages can be sent to the muscles of the body to help preserve balance.

The labyrinth or vestibular apparatus is an intricate structure composed of a gravity-sensitive part (the *utricle* and *saccule*) and three semicircular canals sensitive to rotation of the head. These canals curve upward, sideways and backward, and are filled with fluid. In each there is a slightly expanded region, the *ampulla,* containing a bundle of sensitive nerves projecting into the canal. Rotation of the head swirls the fluid in the canals and pushes these nerves sideways. They then fire off nerve impulses which pass along the vestibular nerve to their cell bodies grouped together in the pons. As there are three canals at right angles to each other, rotary movement in any direction can be detected.

Inside both the utricle and the saccule there is a small ridge, the *macula.* This is made of sensory cells with stiff, calcium-laden projections which rise vertically when the head is upright. Change in posture bends these projections; the cells sense the change, which is signaled to the brain.

Cerebral cortex

Midbrain

Cerebellum

Vestibular nerve

Vestibular nuclei

Medulla

Spinal cord

Semicircular canals

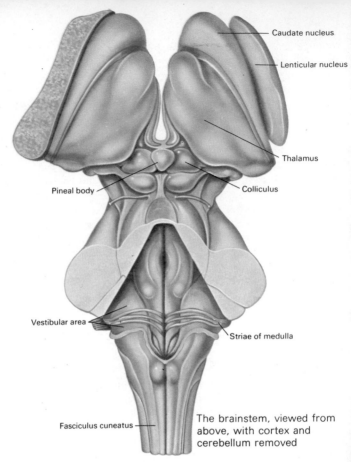

The brainstem, viewed from above, with cortex and cerebellum removed

Labels on image: Caudate nucleus, Lenticular nucleus, Thalamus, Colliculus, Pineal body, Vestibular area, Striae of medulla, Fasciculus cuneatus

The basal ganglia, thalamus, hypothalamus and reticular formation

These groups of neurons around the ventricles in the center of the brain are involved not only with movement and sensation but with thirst, appetite, emotion and temperature.

The *basal ganglia,* comprising the *caudate nucleus, putamen* and *globus pallidus,* are closely linked with structures in the nearby midbrain (the *red nucleus* and *substantia nigra*), with the motor region of the cerebral cortex, and — through the red nucleus — with the spinal cord. Collectively these neuronal groups play an important part in voluntary movement, and when they are diseased the muscles may become slow, weak and rigid. Parkinson's disease, with limited, slow and tremulous movements, results from damage to this system, and it has been treated by an operation in which some of the inner connections of the basal ganglia are severed. Today, drug therapy is replacing surgery in the treatment of Parkinson's disease.

The *thalamus* is situated near the midline and behind the basal ganglia on each side of the third ventricle. It is an egg-shaped mass of nerve cells which receives all the sensory information from the head, limbs and trunk, processes it and transmits it to the sensory area of the cerebral cortex. When the thalamus is damaged, patients lose the experience of light touch and the ability precisely to localize sensations and may feel a severe, burning pain.

Below the thalamus are a few small collections of cells, forming the *hypothalamus.* It regulates heat production and loss by stimulating shivering and sweating. It contains receptors which are sensitive to changes of salt concentration in the blood and control water intake and output through thirst and ADH-secretion (see page 85). Hypothalamic injury may cause emotional outbursts, great overeating with obesity and reduction of sexual activity.

The reticular formation is a poorly defined network of nerve cells and fibers located in the center of the brainstem and passing down from the thalamus to the medulla. It sends axons down the spinal cord to motor neurons and it plays some part in controlling reflexes and muscle tone. In addition it is concerned with sleep and consciousness, for changes in its electrical activity produce changes of wakefulness.

Cross-section of midbrain stained to show fiber tracts (dark) and cell masses (light)

Cerebral aqueduct

Superior colliculus

Sensory ascending tracts

Red nucleus

Substantia nigra

Oculomotor nerve

Corticospinal tract

Motor area

Sensory area

Speech movements

Visual are

Hearing

Left cerebral hemisphere with main functional areas

The cerebral cortex—localization of function

The cerebral hemispheres make up the greater part of the brain and are bigger in man than in any other animal. Man's ascendency over his environment and other species is related to the size of his cerebrum. The cortex, or external layer of gray matter, is crumpled and wrinkled; if stretched out flat it would cover nearly two and a half square feet. It is on the average only 1/8- to 1/10-inch thick, but it contains millions of neurons that are the basis of mind.

Groups of convolutions or *gyri* form separate lobes (see illustration, page 43). The frontal lobes, placed above the orbits, are concerned with personality, behavior and movement. The lowest left frontal gyrus is the center for speech. Further back are the *parietal areas,* which are involved in the analysis of sensations and with the 'body image', that is, recognition of the body in relation to its surroundings. At the back of the head, on top of the cerebellum, are the *occipital lobes,* whose function is visual. On either side of the brain lies a separate projection, like the thumb of a boxer's glove. This is the *temporal lobe,* which interprets auditory information. A curled structure, the *hippocampus,* is hidden inside the temporal lobe and is partly concerned with taste and smell.

In most regions of the cortex, six separate cell layers

can be recognized under the microscope. The outermost (layer 1 in illustration) contains only axons, dendrites and neuroglia. Next come two pairs of layers (2 and 3, 4 and 5) containing small round neurons and large pyramidal neurons, and an inner layer (6) of long spindly cells lying at right angles to the surface. The relative thickness of the layers varies from place to place in the cerebrum, and in certain regions special cell types are found. One of these cell types is the 'giant' pyramidal *Betz cell* of the motor region of the frontal cortex.

The motor area of one hemisphere controls voluntary movements of the other side of the body. Since information about individual movements rather than individual muscles is sent out, and since the range and variety of movements is greater for some parts of the body than for others, the cortex is not equally apportioned to all parts: the more delicate the movements, the larger the cortical area controlling them. Thus the fingers and face are governed by relatively many Betz cells, while the neck and back are controlled by relatively few.

The cortex is protected by the skull, and cushioned by fluid in the cranial membranes (*left*). On the right is a section of the cortex with some cell bodies stained—the layers are numbered as in the text. A Betz cell can be seen in the center.

(*Below*) The relative representation of the body surface on the cortex

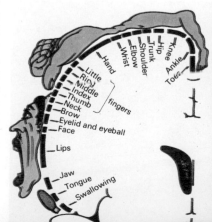

Personality and the prefrontal lobes

One particular part of the cerebral cortex that is very well developed in man is the *prefrontal region,* which lies in front of the motor area. It has no primary sensory or motor functions, but is connected with other cortical regions and with some of the deeper structures of the brain, including the thalamus and hypothalamus; it is involved in the control of emotions and the storage of information, and it is the part of the brain concerned above all with personality and intellect.

Damage to the prefrontal lobes may occur in disease or be produced by accident or by the surgeon in the treatment of some mental disorders. Operations such as *leucotomy* and *lobotomy* cause characteristic behavior changes by interfering with normal function. Judgment is adversely affected and insight is lost, so that self-confidence often rises while ability decreases. A marked feature is loss of concentration; people who have had these operations cannot stick to one task for long. In addition, emotional responses are altered. Emotions are often blunted, but they are sometimes exaggerated, with the result that an everyday situation may produce violent rages or incongruous cheerfulness. These disturbances occur not only in localized damage to the prefrontal lobes but also in any con-

Major association pathways of the cortex

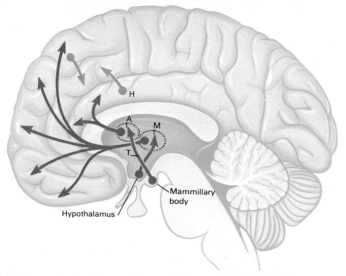

Pathways involved in emotion and memory link the hippocampus, *H*, the prefrontal lobes, the thalamus and hypothalamus and the mamillary body. *A* is the anterior nucleus of the thalamus, *M* the medial nucleus, and *T* is the mamillo-thalamic tract.

The lobes of the cerebral cortex

dition that disturbs the functioning of the cerebral cortex as a whole. The picture of dementia starts with defects of reasoning and judgment and continues with deterioration of social habits—such as language, dress and cleanliness—and emotional instability and impulsive behavior. If the disorder is severe or progressive, the general condition of the body deteriorates as well.

Perception—the parietal lobes

Just as the frontal cortex is the highest control center for voluntary movement, so the parietal lobes are implicated in the most precise aspects of sensation. The sub-station for sensory messages, as has been noted, is the thalamus, and some 'crude' sensations, such as pain and heat, are felt largely at this level. However, the parietal cortex is essential for the recognition of shape, size, surface-texture and the various other qualities that depend on fine discrimination. It also refines the cruder sensations and so helps the body to distinguish different degrees of heat and cold, and it enables sensations to be localized and small amounts of joint movement to be assessed.

Damage to this part of the brain causes a sensory loss that is not intense but which is very disturbing and disabling for the patient. By severing the connections with other regions of the cerebral cortex, it may produce much stranger effects than simple sensory loss; the recognition of an object involves not only the pathways leading to the parietal cortex but also those concerned with memory and with producing the correct response to the incoming information. If the memory or the correct response is missing, what is seen (or heard or felt) will not be recognized. This loss of recognition may extend to the patient himself. Someone with a damaged right parietal lobe may ignore the left side of his body, believing that his left arm and leg do not belong to him, as well as the left side of space, so that he will be aware, for instance, of only the figures 12 to 6 on a clock face.

The illustration shows the loss of vision and awareness of left limbs resulting from a loss of information from the right cortex such as might occur in damage to the right parietal lobe.

Speech and its control

Human beings communicate by uttering sounds that are shaped into meaningful patterns. Such communication, which we call speech, is the means of expressing feelings and thoughts and conveying information and commands. Speech has three main components—the sounds themselves, their shaping or articulation, and their control or ordering.

The *sounds,* the first basic element of speech, are produced in the larynx by the vibration of the vocal cords in the airstream coming from the lungs. The tension of the vocal cords, and thus the pitch of the sounds, is altered by the small muscles of the larynx, activated by the laryngeal nerves; if these nerves are affected in any way, sound production is disturbed and hoarseness may result.

Articulation depends on the muscles of the jaws, lips, tongue and palate, which serve both to alter the shape of the resonating cavities and interrupt the stream of sound. The nerves supplying these muscles originate in the brainstem, but like all voluntary motor activities articulation is under the control

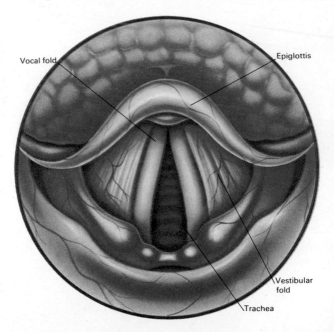

Vocal fold

Epiglottis

Vestibular
fold

Trachea

of the cerebral cortex.

Full control of the muscles of speech ensures that spoken messages are carefully and precisely uttered, but not that they are meaningful. For speech to have a meaning, rather than to consist of random syllables, the whole of one cerebral hemisphere must be working normally. In most people, it is the left hemisphere that is vital for speech; in left-handed people, it is the right one. A localized area in the left inferior frontal gyrus of the cortex is often regarded as the speech control center, for when it is damaged (as happens in strokes) speech is severely impaired. In fact, since the various cortical regions are intricately interconnected, most of the hemisphere is involved in normal speaking. Damage anywhere in it (though particularly in the back half) can cause disturbances of speech. The impossibility of teaching chimpanzees to use more than a very few speech sounds relates to their lack of cerebral organization.

Larynx viewed from above (*opposite*). Dissected rear view of larynx (*above*). Position of tongue for producing consonants G and L (*right*).

147

EEG record during a brief epileptic fit—note the spiky waves during the attack (starting at arrow marked *a*) and the return of the alpha rhythm after eye closure (arrow marked *b*). The changes are clearest in the records from the back of the head.

The EEG and epilepsy

If electrodes are placed in contact with the scalp and connected to sensitive amplifying apparatus, electrical activity originating in the brain is detectable. This activity arises from the simultaneous changes of potential in millions of nerve cells in the cerebral cortex, and it constitutes the *electroencephalogram* (EEG). With practice, different waves can be discerned in the irregular EEG tracing. The basic normal activity is the alpha rhythm, with waves occurring 8 to 13 times a second. In children it is not well marked, but in adults it is often very evident, particularly in recordings made from the back of the head; it increases when the eyes are shut and decreases when they are opened or when a mental effort is made. Beta waves (13 to 20 per second) and theta waves (4 to 7 per second) are also found in the normal EEG, but slow delta activity is always an indication of brain disease.

Epilepsy is a term that covers a variety of fits, ranging from severe convulsions to short-lived blackouts or loss of awareness. In generalized convulsions consciousness is lost, the arms and legs stiffen, and then jerk rhythmically; the

148

tongue may be bitten, and the bladder emptied. The mildest fits often appear to be no more than a brief interruption of attention. Between these extremes are *focal seizures* (where one part of the body is involved); *Jacksonian fits* (in which involuntary movement spreads from a thumb or the corner of the mouth to other regions); and *temporal lobe* attacks. Many fits begin with a premonition or aura, but temporal lobe attacks start with such symptoms as an unpleasant taste or smell, flashing lights, ringing bells or a complete vision.

All fits are due to episodes of excessive electrical activity of the gray matter of the brain; different sorts of fit can be explained in terms of involvement of different parts of the cerebrum. Fits are in some way a constitutional upset and tend to run in families; they can occur without obvious cause or be brought on by brain disease. Whatever their cause, they produce an abnormal EEG tracing, which may contain characteristic spiky waves during or between attacks.

An EEG machine in use

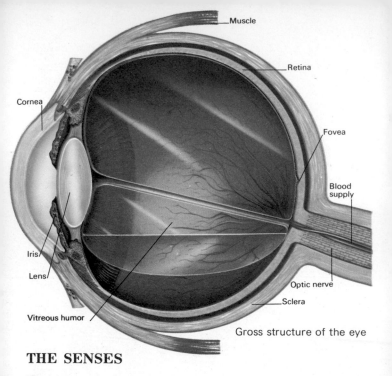

Gross structure of the eye

THE SENSES

The eye

Like the camera, the eye collects and focuses light on a photo-sensitive surface. Its transparent, yellowish, gelatinous lens is much more spherical when removed than when it is in its normal position, flattened by the pull of ligaments on its fibrous covering. Relaxation of these ligaments is produced by contraction of the ciliary muscle at the back of the *iris*—this allows the *lens* to bulge, making nearby objects come into focus. In old age the lens becomes more rigid and far-sightedness results.

The *pupil* is the aperture of the iris, which is an automatic diaphragm opening and closing in response to changes of lighting. Behind the lens the eyeball is filled with a sticky, jelly-like substance, at the back of which is the *retina*. This is the natural counterpart of a photographic film; it is made up of three layers of nerve cells, with the light receptors—the *rods* and *cones*—on the outside. The rods and cones are

An inverted image is focused on the retina. In near sight the image falls before the retina, while in far sight the image is focused behind the retina. (*above*)

the extensions of small neurons, and they convert light into nerve impulses, which are passed to the brain along the fibers of the *optic nerve*. Where the optic nerve leaves the eye there are no receptors; this 'blind spot' is slightly off the axis of vision. The center of the retina possesses only cones connected to nerve fibers in a 1:1 ratio. Out from the center, rods increase in number, receptors converging onto fewer fibers. Since rods work at low light intensity (they contain an easily bleached pigment—*rhodopsin*—derived from vitamin A) the periphery of the retina is adapted for sensitivity in dim light, the center for detailed, daylight vision.

Objects to the left are seen by both eyes but projected to the right visual cortex (*middle*) Organization of receptor and nerve cells in retina (*bottom*)

Color vision depends upon the mixing of the messages from three types of cone corresponding to the three primary colors.

Visual area

A typical card used to test for color blindness

Nerve impulses pass back to the lateral geniculate body in the thalamus, whence they are relayed to the occipital cortex, and to the *superior colliculus,* which is concerned with control of eye movement. Fibers from the outer half of the retina stay on the same side while those from the inner half cross the midline. Since the image formed on the retina is upside down, each half-field of vision, left or right, projects onto the opposite cortex.

We see colors by virtue of possessing retinal cones sensitive to either red or blue or green, the three primary colors, from mixtures of which all other colors can be produced. Thus receptors of the three types are stimulated according to the proportion of each primary in the light falling on them. Color blindness is of various sorts, but in a common variety red cannot be recognized and probably the red-sensitive cones are defective. To see colors perfectly depends on the cortex, which 'corrects' the imperfect, blurred and color-distorted images produced by the primitive lens of the eye, just as it constructs a 'solid' image from the slightly dissimilar ones from each eye.

The ear and the mechanics of hearing

There is an outer, a middle and an inner ear. The outer ear funnels sounds onto the eardrum, making it vibrate. The vibrations are transmitted to the three bones of the middle ear, the *malleus* (hammer), *incus* (anvil) and *stapes* (stirrup), which are linked to each other, to the drum on the outside and the oval window of the *cochlea* (inner ear) on the inside. This oval window has only 1/16 of the area of the ear drum and the three bones act as a mechanical linkage to concentrate the sound vibrations onto it. The cochlea is placed deep in the bone of the side of the skull. Cochlea means snail, and it is in fact a fluid-filled tube coiled two-and-a-half times around a central core of bone. The cochlea connects with the middle ear at the oval and round windows, covered respectively with the bony foot of the stapes and with a membrane, and contains the actual organ of hearing, the *organ of Corti*. This is a collection of specialized sensory nerve processes resting on a centrally placed layer of fibers, the *basilar membrane*.

Structures of the inner, middle and outer ear

153

The sense endings in the cochlea respond to movement of the tectorial membrane.

Scala vestibuli

Cochlear duct

Scala tympani

Sensitive hair cells

Supporting cells

Tectorial membrane

Auditory nerve

Auditory nerve   Basilar membrane

The vibrations transmitted from the outer ear to the foot of the stapes cause corresponding minute pressure changes in the fluid of the cochlea. These pressure waves return to the middle ear at the round window after spiraling around the cochlea and activating the organ of Corti. What happens is that the sounds (or pressure waves) cause a traveling wave to appear in the basilar membrane, like the wave traveling along a loosely held jumping rope when one end is jerked. The size and speed of this wave depend on the pitch (frequency) and the loudness (amplitude) of the sound. Movement of the underlying membrane stimulates the receptors on top to fire off nerve impulses. Different parts of the cochlea are sensitive to different sounds, high and low, and this difference is such that the wave produced by a particular sound excites the appropriate part of the organ of Corti.

Taste and smell

The sensations of taste and smell depend on the physical and chemical properties of the substances that produce them. They involve the attachment of small quantities of the substance in question—no more than a few molecules for some smells—to the sensory receptors of the mouth, palate and nose.

The receptors for taste are found on the upper surface of the

154

glottis

ter

ur

eet and salt

Sensory hair

Taste cells

Supporting cells

Nerve fibers

The taste buds (*right*) are selectively sensitive to stimuli and are unevenly distributed over the tongue.

tongue and in the palate and throat. The *taste buds* are probably of four kinds, since four basic tastes—sweet, sour, salt and bitter—are recognizable in different regions of the tongue. Structurally the buds appear the same, consisting of a nest of elongated cells connected to a sensory nerve. Messages are relayed to the parietal and temporal cortex.

The nerves of smell, the *olfactory nerves,* lie in a yellow area lining the uppermost part of the nose cavity. They are the extensions of nerve cells whose central branches pass upward through the bone of the skull to join the olfactory bulbs. These are situated below the frontal lobes and contain more nerve cells, the axons of which send on the sensory messages to the innermost gyri of the temporal lobes.

Endings of smell are situated in the nasal cavity.

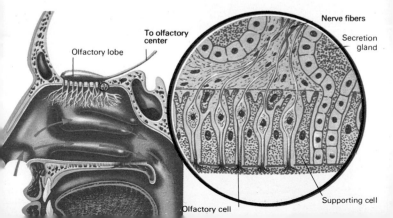

Nerve fibers

Secretion gland

To olfactory center

Olfactory lobe

Olfactory cell

Supporting cell

BOOKS TO READ

The Human Body. Isaac Asimov, Houghton Mifflin, 1963.

The Wonders of The Human Body. Martin L. Keen. Grosset & Dunlap, 1966.

Human Anatomy and Physiology. Barry G. King and Mary Jane Showers. W. B. Saunders, 1963.

The Science Book of the Human Body. Edith E. Sproul. Franklin Watts, 1955.

Magic, Myth and Medicine. Donald T. Atkinson, Fawcett World Library, 1958 (paperback).

A Short History of Anatomy and Physiology from the Greeks to Harvey. Charles Singer. Dover, 1957 (paperback).

Medicine and Man. Ritchie Calder. New American Library, 1958 (paperback).

Nerves and Muscles. Robert Galambos. Doubleday Anchor Books, 1962 (paperback).

The Senses of Animals and Men. Lorus J. and Margery Milne. Atheneum, 1962.

The Computer and The Brain. John Von Neumann. Yale University Press, 1958.

So You Want to Be A Doctor. Alan E. Nourse. Harper & Row, 1963.

The Great Doctors. Henry E. Sigerist. Doubleday Anchor Books, 1958 (paperback).

INDEX

Page numbers in bold type refer to illustrations.

Acetylcholine 51, 87, 129
ACTH 85, 89, **89**
Action potential
 see Nerve impulse
Actomyosin 126
Addison's disease 82, 88
Adenosine diphosphate (ADP) 62
Adenosine triphosphate (ATP) 62, 126
ADH *see* Antidiuretic hormone
Adrenal cortex 28, 82-86, **83, 84, 86, 87,** 88-89, **89**
Adrenal medulla 26, **26, 28-29, 29,** 86-88, **86, 87**
Adrenalin 29, 86-87, **87**
Albumin 54, **114,** 115
Aldosterone **26,** 28, 78, 88-89
Alveolus 35, **36, 36,** 37, **37,** 40
Amino acids 58, 61, 62, **63**
Amylase 58
Anal sphincter 61
Anemia 41, 110-111, **110-111**
Anoxia **41,** 43
Antibody 99, 107, 113, **114,** 115, 118-119
Antidiuretic hormone 79, 85
Antigen 118-119
Aorta 15, 16, **17, 18,** 19, 20, **21, 25**
Aortic valve **18,** 19, 23
'Apex beat' 16
Appetite 67, **67**
Arteriole 16, **16, 17,** 25
Artery 16, **16,** 19, 24
Artificial kidney 79, 80
Artificial respiration 44-45, **44, 45**
Ascorbic acid 74
Atrio-ventricular node 22, **22**
Atrium 17, 18, **18,** 19, **19,** 20, **20,** 21, 22
Auerbach's plexus 51
Axon 123, **123,** 128

Basal ganglia 121, 135, 138-139
Beri-beri **72,** 73
Bile 52, 53, 55
Bile duct 53, **53**
Bladder 76-77, **76,** 79
Blood 106-119
 circulation of 16-21
 oxygenation of 36-41, **37, 38, 39, 40, 41**
 pressure 24-32, **25**

Blood coagulation 107, 116-117, **116, 117**
Blood groups 118-119, **118, 119**
Bone 12, 13, **13,** 74, 75
Bone marrow 108-110, **108, 109, 110, 111**
Bowman's capsule 77, 78
Brain 120-122, **120**
Brainstem 121, 136, **138**
Bronchitis 40
Bronchus **14, 35, 35**
Brunner's glands 57
'Bundle of His' 22

Calcium 65, 93-95
Calorie 63, 64, **64-65**
Cancer 69
Capillary 16, **16, 17,** 18, 36, 38, 74
Carbohydrates **60,** 61, **63, 66**
Carbon dioxide 32, 37–39, **37, 39,** 62-63, **63**
Cardiac cycle 20-21, **24**
Cardiac sphincter 49
Carotene 70
Carotid artery **42,** 43
Carotid chemoreceptor **42,** 43
Cartilage 12-13, **13**
Cell 4-13, **4, 5,** 39, **54,** 81
Centrosome **7**
Cerebellum 120, **120,** 121, 135, **135,** 136, **137**
Cerebral cortex 120-121, **120,** 132, 136, 140-143, **140, 141, 142, 143,** 148
Cerebral ventricles 121, 125, 138
Cerebrospinal fluid 125
Cerebrum *see* Cerebral cortex
Cholesterol 75
Cholinesterase 129
Chromosome 6, **6-7,** 100, **100**
Cilium, **34**
Circulation 14-31, **17**
Clotting *see* Blood coagulation
Cochlea 153-154, **153, 154**
Collagen 11, **11,** 13
Colon 58
Color vision 151-152, **152**
Cone 151, **151, 152**
Connective tissue 8, 11, **11,** 74
Cornea **72**
Coronary artery 20
Corpus luteum 101-103, **102**
Cortical lobes 140
 frontal 140, 142-143
 parietal 144
 temporal 155

Corticosteroids 88-89, **89**
Cortisone 88-89
Cretinism 92
Curare 129
Cushing's disease **88,** 89
Cyanocobalamin 72
Cyanosis 41
Cytoplasm 5, **7,** 11, 61

Dendrite **122,** 123
Deoxyribonucleic acid (DNA) 6
Dermis 10, **10**
Diabetes 68, 82, 85, 89, 96-98
Diaphragm **14,** 15, 32, 33, **33,** 34, 42
Diastole 20, 24
Diet 64-75, **68-69**
Digestion 48-62
Duodenum 53, 56-57, **57**

Ear 153-154, **153, 154**
Edema 73
Elastic fiber **11,** 13
Electrocardiogram (EKG) 22, **22, 23**
Electroencephalogram (EEG) 148-149, **148, 149**
Electrolytes 81
Electrophoresis **114,** 115
Embryo 103
Endocrine *see* Hormones
Endoplasmic reticulum **4,** 5
Enzyme 5, 41, **41,** 46, 54, 57, 70
Epidermis 10, **10**
Epiglottis 34, **34**
Epilepsy 148-149, **148**
Epithelium 8-10, **8, 49,** 70, 73
Esophagus 48, 49, **49**
Estrogen 101-103, **102**
Eye **27,** 70, **72,** 150-151, **150, 151,** 152

Fainting 30-31
Fallopian tubes 101-102, **101**
Fat 54, 55, 57, **60,** 61, 63, **63, 66**
Fatty acids 57, 62
Feces 58
Fetus 103, **103**
Fibrinogen 55, 116-117, **117**
Folic acid 72
Follicle 10, **10**
Fructase 58

Gall bladder 53, **53**
Gallstones 68
Gene 6
Globulin 54, **114,** 115
Glomeruli 77, **77,** 78
Glucagon 98

Glucose 61, 62, 97-98, 126
Glycerol 57, 62
Glycogen 54, 62, 97-98, 126
Golgi body **4, 5**

Hair 10, **10**
Heart **14,** 15-16, **15, 18,** 19-23, 40-41
Heart block 31
Heart murmur 23
Hemoglobin 38, **38,** 39, **39,** 40, 41, 106, 110–111, **110**
Hemophilia **116,** 117
Hepatic artery 52, 53
Hepatic ducts 52-53, **52 53**
Hepatic vein 52
Hippocampus 140, 143, **143**
'Hole in the heart' 40
Holger–Nielsen *see* Artificial respiration
Hormones 82-105
Hydrochloric acid 50
Hydrocortisone 88
Hypertension 26-28
Hypothalamus 46-47, 85-86, **87,** 139, **143**

Ileum 58
Insulin 89, 96-98, **96, 98**
Intercostal muscles 32, **32,** 33, 34, 35, 42
Intercostal nerves 42
Intermittent positive pressure respiration 45
Intestine, large 58, **59,** small 56, **56,** 57, 58, **59**
Invertase 61
Iodine 65, 90-92, **93**
Iron 65, 106, 110-111

Jejunum 58
Joint 13, **13**

Kidney 26, **27,** 28, 76-81, **76, 77**

Labyrinth 136-137, **136 137**
Lactase 61
Lactic acid 126
Langerhans, islets of 57, 96-98, **97**
Larynx **14,** 34, 146, **146, 147**
Lens 150, **150,** 152
Lipase 58, 62
Liver 52-55, **52, 54, 55,** 70
Lung **14, 15, 17, 32,** 33, 35, **35,** 36, **37,** 38, 40
Lymph node 112-114, **112, 113**
Lymphocyte 99, **107,** 109, 112-114

Malnutrition 69
Maltase 58, 61
Maltose 57
Medulla 42, 121, 135, 139
Meiosis 6
Meissner's plexus 51

Melanin 10
Melanoblast 10
Menopause 101
Menstruation 101-102, **102**
Mesentery 58
Metabolism 61, 62-63, 78
Midbrain 121, 134, 138-139, **139**
Mitochondrion 5
Mitosis 6
Mitral valve **18,** 19, 23
Monocyte **107,** 109, 114
Mouth-to-mouth respiration **44,** 45
Mucin 48
Mucous membrane 57
Mucus **34,** 50, 58
Mucus gland **34**
Muscle, skeletal 126-127, **126** smooth 50-51
Myelin **124,** 125, **128**
Myxoedena 92, **92**

Nasal lining **34**
Nephron 77, 78
Nerve cell *see* Neuron
Nerve impulse 123, 128-129, **128**
Nervous system 120-155, **120, 121**
Neuroglia 123, 124, 125, **125,** 141
Neuromuscular junction 128–129, **129**
Neuron **122-123,** 123, 134
Nicotinamid 72, 73
Noradrenalin 26, **26,** 29, **28-29,** 86-87, **87**
Nucleic acids 58
Nucleoprotein 63
Nucleus **4,** 5, 6

Obesity 68, **69**
Organ of Corti 153-154, **154**
Organelle 5
Osmosis 80
Osteoarthritis 68
Ovaries **83,** 84, **84, 89,** 101-103, **101**
Ovulation 102, **102**
Ovum 5, 101-103, **102**
Oxygen 32, 36-43, **37, 39, 40, 41, 42**
Oxytocin **84,** 85

Pacemaker 31, **31**
Pancreas 53, **53,** 56, 57, 82, 96-98, **97**
Parasympathetic nervous system 88
Parathyroid 90, **91,** 94-95, **94**
Parotid gland 48
Pellagra 73, **73**
Pepsin 50
Perception 144
Periosteum 12
Peristalsis 49, **51,** 61
Peritoneum 56, **57**
Peritonitis 56

Personality 142
Pharynx **34**
Phosphate 65, 94
Phrenic nerves 42
Pituitary 82-85, **83, 84, 85,** 89, 102, **102**
Placenta 103, **103**
Plasma 38, 55, 81, 107, 114-116, **114,** 116
Platelets **106,** 107, 116-117, **117**
Pleura **15, 32,** 35
Pleurisy 35
Poliomyelitis 45
Polycythaemia 27-28
Polypeptides 50, 57
Pons 121, 135
Portal vein 52, 53
Potassium 65, 81, 128, **128**
Pregnancy 102-103
Progesterone 101-103, **102**
Protein 54, 57, **60,** 61, **63,** 66
Prothrombin 55, 75, 116, **117**
Ptyalin 48, 61
Pulmonary artery 16, **18, 21**
Pulmonary valve **18,** 19, 23
Pupil 150, **150**
Pylorus 50, 51
Pyridoxin 72

Ranvier, node of 125, **125,** 129
Receptors, sensory 124, 130-133, **130,** 150-151, **151, 154,** 153–155, **155**
Rectum 58
Red cell 38, 55, **106,** 107-111, **110, 111,** 116, 118, 119
Reflex 132-133, **133**
Renal cortex **76,** 77
Renal medulla **76,** 77
Renal pelvis 76, 77, **76,** 79
Renal tubule 77, **77**
Renal vein 76
Renin 26–27
Respiration 32-45
Respiratory center 42, **42,** 43, **43**
Reticular formation 139
Reticulo-endothelial cells 55
Retina 27, 70, 150-152, **150, 151**
Rhesus **118,** 119
Rhodopsin 70, 151
Rib 14, 15, **32,** 33
Rib-cage 15, 33, 35
Riboflavin 72, 73
Ribonucleic acid (RNA) 5
Rickets 75, **75**
Rod 151, **151**

Saliva 48
Schwann cell **124,** 125
Scurvy 74, **74**
Sebaceous gland 10
Semicircular canal **137,** 137
Serum 107, 116, 119, **119**
Sex determination 100, **100**

Shivering 46
Shock 28-29
Sino-artrial node 22, **22**
Sinusoid 53, 55
Skin 10, **10**
Sleep 139
Smell 154-155, **155**
Sodium 65, 81, 128, **128**
Speech 146-147
Spermatozoon 104-105, **104**
Spinal cord 42, 120-122, **120, 121,** 132-133, **133,** 136
Spinal nerves 120, **121,** 122
Spleen 111, 113-114, **113**
Steatorrhea 55, 69
Stomach 50, **50,** 51
Sublingual gland 48
Submandibular gland 48
Swallowing 48
Sweat gland 9, **10,** 10
Sweating 10, 46
Sympathetic nervous system 15, 22, 29, 51, 86-87
Synapse **122,** 123, **131**
Systole 20, 24

Taste 154-155, **155**
Taste bud 154-155, **155**
Temperature regulation 46, **47**
Tendon 11
Testes 84, **84, 89,** 104-105, **104, 105**
Testosterone 104
Thalamus 139, **143,** 144
Thiamin 72-73
Thorax 14-16, **14, 15, 32**
Thromboplastin 116-117, **117**
Thymus 99, **99**
Thyrocalcitonin 93
Thyroid 82, **83,** 84, **84,** 90-93
Thyrotoxicosis 91, **92**
Thyroxin 91-92
Tongue 48, 154-155, **155**
Trachea **14, 32,** 34-35, **34**
Tricuspid valve **18,** 19, 23

Urea 54, 63, **63**
Ureter 76, **76,** 79

Urine 76-77, 78, **78,** 79
Uterus 101-103, **101, 102**

Vagus nerve 15, 22, 31, 51
Vasoconstriction 46
Vasodilatation 46
Vasomotor center 25, 29
Vein **16, 17,** 18
Vena cava 15, **17,** 18, **18,** 76
Ventricle 16, **17,** 19, **19,** 20, **20-21,** 22, 23
Venule **16, 17,** 18
Vertebrae 14
Villi 57, **59**
Vital capacity 36
Vitamins 55, 70-75, **71**
Vocal cords 146, **147**
Vomiting 51

Water 80, **80, 81**
White cell **106,** 107-109, **107, 111,** 112-114, **112**

Special Offer

Paul Lewis and **David Rubenstein** combine their expertise to provide this concise book on how the human body functions. Paul Lewis is a medical lecturer and consultant neurologist and David Rubenstein is a biological research scientist.